# The Weather Report

# The Weather Report

Donald P. DeNevi

Celestial Arts
Millbrae, California

photo credits:  NOAA:  28, 29, 30, 31, 32, 33, 37, 41, 43, 44, 45,
                85, 92, 94, 95, 96, 97, 98, 100, 111, 121, 123
                Ames Research Center:  63
                U.S. Dept. of Agriculture:  97
                NASA:  33, 122

Cover design by Betsy Bruno

Celestial Arts
231 Adrian Road
Millbrae, California 94030

First Printing, March 1978

Made in the United States of America


**Library of Congress Cataloging in Publication Data**

DeNevi, Donald P.
    The weather report.

    Bibliography; p.
    Includes index.
    1.  Climatic changes.     2.  Weather.
I.  Title.
QC981.8.C5D4     551.6     77-90007
ISBN 0-89087-205-8


1   2   3   4   5   6—84   83   82   81   80   79   78

# Contents

*The greater man's "mastery" of nature, the more essential is his understanding of causes in order that mastery be disciplined to obedience*

Harvey Brooks

# Dedication

If there is to be a dedication to this book, it should serve as a recognition of the members of the U.S. Committee for the Global Atmospheric Research Program and its Panel on Climatic Variation. Of these members, J. Murray Mitchell and Jerome Namias are to be singled out. Along with their colleagues, their objectives have been to advance the state of atmospheric sciences and technology in order to provide greater knowledge of the basic physical forces affecting climate. The day will soon arrive when they will have developed long-range weather forecasting atmospheric science research which will complement the program fostered by the World Meteorological Organization.

And, more humbly, this book is dedicated to the *contadini* of America, especially Jerome Vernazza and Aldo DeNevi, men of the soil and produce who above all know the awesomeness of climatic change. . . .

# Introduction

Our earth, a mosaic of multi-colored patterns of land, sea, and atmosphere, is a unique combination of physical, chemical, and biological interactions exactly suited for its inhabitants. Swirling in the vacuum of space, and perhaps alone as far as human life is concerned, the planet brought tragic death to hundreds of thousands by starvation and freezing during the middle 1970s. Earth employed a simple means for the killing and crippling of millions of others—scientists have called that means *climate.*

Climate can be simply defined as the weather with all its variations over a long period of time. When climatic changes occur, as our dynamic planet continues to grow and develop, death, critical illness, and misery follow. Even without changes in weather, millions live out shortened lives, their physical frailties a mismatch to the environments in which they find themselves.

Now, for the first time in history, man has come to realize the fragile nature of his planetary environment. The land, sea, and air are not boundless resources, as once tacitly supposed. Man cannot simply take the fish at will, gouge the land, or pollute the air without paying an increasing price. On the other hand, man must feed his family, he must live, and, he can only survive by his ability to use what is necessary from his surroundings. How much can he take? How much must he leave? And, above all, how will Mother Nature behave? When fooling with her, will she employ her traditionally quiet way of using weather to kill?

These are the kinds of questions being asked by those who think and plan not only for the present, but also for the future. To acquire answers, it will be necessary to employ all the research tools at man's disposal. Scientists must analyze each component of the climatic system, which includes not only the atmosphere but the world's oceans, the ice masses, and the exposed land surface itself. In this way they expect to make significant advances in the understanding of the elusive and complex processes of climatic change.

The mission of this book is to offer a look into a vital part of the American effort to answer these questions. With the help and criticism of Dr. J. Murray Mitchell, Jr., Senior Research Climatologist of the National Oceanic and Atmospheric Administration's Environmental Data Service, the following pages have been written to improve the comprehension of climatic variation and uses of the physical environment and its oceanic life. Hopefully, the book will serve as a source of objective information on weather shifts, climatic change, and the effects man's actions may have on environmental quality.

Donald P. DeNevi
Merritt College

# I

# Climate's Madness: A World of Ice, Drought, and Cataclysm

*Some say the world will end in fire,*
*Some say in ice.*

Robert Frost

Will the world end precipitously?

Everywhere, mute testimonials to the tremendous power of climate suggest as much. Never before in recorded history has mankind been so completely at the mercy of the weather. Cooling in the northern hemisphere; thawing in the Antarctic; shifting belts of drought, rain, snow, storm patterns; dramatic increases, decreases, and changes in ice caps; volcanic dust; air pollution; and sunspots have worried scientists searching for intelligent answers around the globe. People, animals, and machines, over various parts of the globe have been immobilized under heavy blankets of snow, ice, or heat.

The myriad forces that can change the earth's basic environment are not understood very well. That the earth's climate changes is accepted by all earth scientists, from meteorologists to anthropologists. The three key questions facing worried climate experts are: Is the earth as a whole cooling off, and therefore heading into another disastrous ice age? Or, because of mankind's polluting industries, machines, automobiles, and agricultural practices, could we instead be heating the atmosphere of our planet? What kinds of climates will our grandchildren and great-grandchildren experience? The answers to such complex questions on what's happening to our weather will determine the fate of our planet and its hundreds of millions of people.

Today, climatic change is a matter of grave concern to all scientists. More than any other group of people, scientists are deeply conscious of the fact that our whole economic and social stability is profoundly influenced by climate and that mankind's own activities are capable of influencing the weather in very undesirable and, generally, unpredictable ways. Recently, in certain regions climatic extremes have persisted for several weeks, months, and even years. Excessive droughts, rains, winds, and snows, along with severely high and low temperatures, are leading experts to consider economic and social adjustments on a worldwide scale. This is because the current global patterns of food production and population have evolved on the climates of past centuries.

It is not the swift advance of major ice sheets over farms, cities, states, and continents which have earth scientists concerned, but the persistent temperature and rainfall changes in geographic areas heavily committed to agricultural use and development. For example, changes in the frost content of Canadian and Siberian soils, as well as changes in ocean temperature areas of high agricultural production are of more serious, immediate concern than a devastating ice age which would probably take thousands of years to evolve. The coming of a new ice age would be gradual and almost imperceptible.

In the decades and centuries just ahead, the fluctuations of climate over shorter periods of time are likely to be so great as to obscure the long-term trend toward the next ice age. Shorter-term climate changes may, however, be due to unnatural, or man-made, causes, as well as to natural ones. These require urgent attention and careful study. The world's food production is totally dependent on the occurrence of favorable weather conditions during the growing seasons in the world's breadbasket areas. During 1972, a tragically low crop harvest in the Ukraine had immediate international consequences because world grain reserves were but a few percent of annual consumption. The extensive droughts in various parts of Asia and Central Africa during the 1975-1977 years has produced untold suffering and hardship resulting in countless deaths and the migration of millions of people.

Thus, in spite of remarkable advances in technology, food supplies are still highly dependent upon climate. As the world's population continues to grow and as the economic development of emerging nations rises, the need for food, water, and energy will increase dramatically, while the ability to meet those needs remains at the mercy of the weather's vagaries.

But it's not only the demand for food that illustrates the human race's total dependence upon climate—floods, droughts, and temperature extremes seriously disrupt communities, interfere with agriculture, industry, and commerce, and stifle social and economic development. Virtually all of the land most suitable for grazing and agriculture has already been attached. Most of the world's fisheries are being tapped at rates near or above those of natural replenishment. As we approach full use of the earth's water, land, and air, which supply our food and receive our wastes, everyone becomes increasingly dependent on the stability of the present so-called "normal" climate. Our vulnerability to weather change is all the more serious when we recognize that our present climate is in fact highly *abnormal*.

Evidence of the climatic conditions of the earth in past decades, centuries, millennia, and geological epochs, has been deduced from an incredible variety of direct and indirect sources. All the evidence clearly shows that climate variations have occurred on all scales of time. Most earth scientists insist that since the climate has been so continuously variable throughout the past due to natural causes, it has to be assumed that it will continue to vary in the future. However, long-term trends in global climate are masked by shorter-term fluctuations and by regional changes. Exceptionally wet or warm conditions in one region are often accompanied by unusually dry or cool conditions in another area.

The natural shorter-term climatic changes are of increasing importance, as the world's welfare is dependent on weather. It is this short-term variability which in the last few years has been highlighted by the cataclysmic droughts and other disastrous weather extremes. Air pollution could produce a long-term warming and as a consequence, large-scale changes in rainfall distribution. The release into the atmosphere of chlorofluoromethanes and other chemicals, along with the increase in the dust content, could also significantly alter the climate. Direct thermal emissions from industrial and urban areas have already affected local climates, for example, in cities which are several degrees warmer than their surroundings. With the present state of knowledge of the atmosphere, it is not possible to accurately assess the magnitude or impact of such changes resulting from man's activities.

All of climate's current madness has issued a warning signal that mankind simply cannot afford to be unprepared for either a natural or man-made climate catastrophe. Being sensitive to that warning signal, meteorologists and earth scientists have already taken giant steps to improve the quality and accessibility of data relating to past behavior of the atmosphere, the oceans, and other relevant environment factors.

They are seeking to intensify the research into and improve the monitoring of current climatic developments and environmental changes to assess the impact of natural processes and of man's activities.

A reduction of man's physical dependency on climate requires coordinated management of the world's and America's resources on the one hand and a thorough knowledge of the climate's behavior on the other. For example, an accurate assessment of the probability of the occurrence of rainfall within given ranges can provide an assessment of the viability of proposed agricultural or hydrological projects. If the results of further research by meteorologists and other scientists demonstrate that man's activities could produce changes in climate having deadly results for mankind, political and economic decision-makers could act.

It is therefore crucial that we acquire a far greater understanding of climate and climatic change than now we possess. This knowledge will permit a rational response to climatic variations, including an assessment beforehand of man-made influences upon the climate. Understanding our climate will make possible an orderly economic and social adjustment to changes in climate. In short, governments could respond to changes due to variability if sufficient advance warning could be given.

### Climatic Change Strangles the United States

In 1977, while the eastern half of the nation shivered under the bitterest cold in a half-century and the west grew desperately close to severe water rationing in the worst drought in memory, Americans wondered what was going on. Startled millionaires wintering in their baronial villas in West Palm Beach, Florida, couldn't understand why rain had turned to snow. In Dallas, pedestrians were slipping on unaccustomed sleet-slicked sidewalks. In Marin County, across the Golden Gate Bridge just north of San Francisco, human beings were already being rationed to 47 gallons of water a day (flushing a toilet alone consumes nearly nine gallons). Meanwhile, citizens in Buffalo, New York, were slogging through snowdrifts after having been buried with an astonishing 127 inches of snow from a series of violent blizzards.

From the entire Pacific west coast to the Dakotas, spanning the frozen Great Lakes and extending over to New York and all the way down the shivering Eastern seaboard to Florida, the winter of 1977 was already one of the most frightening the United States ever experienced.

The dramatically shifting weather patterns were making their presence felt in both personal and economic hardship. If there was too much winter in some sections of the nation, there was too little elsewhere. A shortage of water in the drought-stricken west was imperiling winter wheat and other crops. Anxieties were mounting that hydroelectric power in the Pacific northwest would all but shut down by mid-summer. In Washington and Oregon, forest fires were already breaking out. In Anchorage, meanwhile, the thermometer was up to a comparatively balmy 45°, the ice so thin and soft that skiers and hockey players went home in disgust. Rocky Mountain ski resort operators complained bitterly that snow storms were avoiding their normally blanketed snow areas. Sun Valley, the mecca of the rich and sedate, was forced to employ snow-making machines for the first time in its history, and at that managed to open only four of its sixty-two runs.

While the brutal and unrelenting arctic cold besieged major metropolitan cities (Cincinnati with 30° below zero; Chicago with 19° below; Dayton with 21° below; New York City with 10° below), economists were estimating that millions of workers had already been laid off—not only because of the icy grip but also because of a dire shortage of natural gas. Long predicted, but totally ignored, the shortage had gone so far as to force hundreds of thousands of already beleaguered people from their snow-covered homes. To most of the unfortunate victims, it was like living in the frozen Arctic. To a few, it was an ominous reminder of how contemporary man, so elated with his technological mastery of the environment, is still at the mercy of Mother Nature. Modern man's almost exclusive reliance on energy-consuming vehicles, machines, and other conveniences was actually contributing to his suffering. Utility companies were deliberately ordering temporary blackouts and reducing voltages throughout mid-western and eastern states in order to meet the soaring energy demands for heating.

The winter's natural gas crisis was delivering a powerful point: the long-expected energy crunch in the United States had arrived. Industry suppliers immediately put into effect emergency pleas, cutting all deliveries to thousands of industrial users. Officials pleaded for schools to close down and for shorter business hours. For a nation standing on the verge of recovering from its sustained economic pause during the 1974-1976 years, the economy was also being tuned down to teeth-chattering levels. The growth rate for 1977's first quarter was scaled down half a percentage point to 5 percent. President Jimmy Carter's economic package of $31.2 billion spread over twenty months was seriously jeopardized. Added to this, food costs were soaring as shifting weather patterns brought cold blights to fruits, vegetables, and livestock feed. Some economists believed that the inflation rate for the first quarter of 1977 could climb as high as 10 percent, compared to the 4.2 percent during the final quarter of 1976.

Because of the devastating climatic changes during the fall of 1976 and winter of 1977, Americans were faced with their choice of disasters: snow, ice, drought,or the torrential floods sure to come when spring's warming weather arrived. And, to make matters worse, the only forecast climatologists could come up with during this time of climatic uncertainty was "no change."

*Forecast: No Change in Continuing Climatic Uncertainty*

What on earth was happening to the weather?

Among the world's meteorologists and climatologists, there was agreement on the immediate reason for the climatic changes across the United States, from the drought-stricken Pacific west coast to the bitter cold of the Eastern seaboard.It seems that the high-level westerly winds (including the long meandering current of high-speed wind, the crucial jet stream) whistling through the upper levels of the atmosphere above the United States and Canada have been circulating in extremely unusual patterns. During the fall and winter months, these winds normally flow directly across the nation from west to east. However, during the winter of 1977, they looped over the Rockies hundreds and sometimes thousands of miles to the north. Then, as they cut toward the east coast, the high-level westerly winds suddenly dipped much farther south than usual. The result of such an unpredictable pattern was the winter's mad weather.

For some unexplained reason, the jet stream had picked up the Pacific storms and guided them across the United States. The resulting heavy snow which buried the eastern part of the country further refrigerated Arctic air masses as they blew down from Canada. The freezing snow blankets also aided the dramatic difference between land and water temperatures, which in turn sparked more storms along the east coast. Meanwhile, the western part of the country remained relatively untouched, leading some scientists to conclude that the winter of 1977 got stuck east of the Rockies.

The mystery of what controls and triggers these

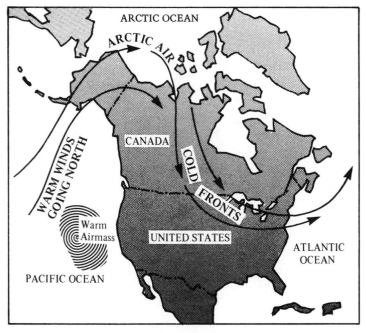

Winter of 1977

changes, and which way they will go next, may well be the most important question yet asked about our earth. For example, some meteorologists and climatologists (meteorologists are primarily concerned with atmospheric processes and the distribution of different kinds of weather; climatologists deal chiefly with the *results* of atmospheric processes) point out that water temperatures in the Pacific rose a few degrees higher than normal off the west coast during the fall of 1976, while temperatures dropped off in the mid-Pacific. Such temperature shifts influence the winds, they say, and determine the course of storms which work their way up into the jet-stream levels. Other scientists blame the storms and frigid temperatures on the high-pressure

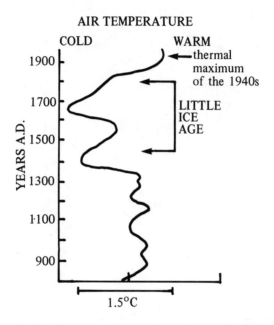

zones of the huge warm air masses hovering off the Pacific west coast which occasionally will shift over land.

When asked what climatic changes are taking place around the country, Dr. J. Murray Mitchell, Jr., Senior Research Climatologist of the National Oceanic and Atmospheric Administration answered, "From 1880 to about 1940, the world, and particularly the northern hemisphere, went through a period of significant warming. But since then, there has been a distinct drop in average global temperature. It's fallen about half a degree Fahrenheit—even more in high latitudes of the northern hemisphere."

For example, Britain's annual growing season shrank by ten to twelve days between 1951 and 1967. In the northern section of the midwestern United States, summer frosts were occasionally damaging wheatfields and other agricultural crops, during the same period. And, along Iceland's coasts, sea ice had returned after more than half a century's absence. Scandinavian, as well as Alaskan, glaciers were no longer melting as fast, while in Switzerland, glaciers actually began advancing again.

In spite of the world's temperatures falling during the last 25 to 40 years, the winters in 1973 through 1975 in sections of the eastern United States and western Russia, as well as much of Europe from 1973 through 1975, were the warmest in 30 years. Recent evidence has suggested that the southern hemisphere was also warming up at the time.

Among those scientists who fear that significant worldwide climatic changes have already begun, there are a few who believe that another ice age is not too far ahead. The ice age doomsayers note that the average snow and ice cover in the northern hemisphere increased sharply in 1970-1971 compared with the years between 1967 and 1970. Reaching a peak in early 1973, it then retreated about halfway back to the level it had been in the late '60s. Scientists say that satellite studies reveal that the snow and ice cover in 1977 increased again to the 1971 level. Meanwhile, German oceanographers have noticed a gradual, slow cooling of the waters in both the north Pacific and north Atlantic, as well as air temperature drops in the arctic regions over Siberia, Alaska, and western Canada.

To the doomsayers, global cooling is explained by a link between ice ages and changes both in the earth's attitude and in its orbit around the sun. Championed by Germany's Alfred Wegener (internationally known for his concepts about the nature of continental drift), the global cooling theory has come into wide circulation. Yugoslavia's mathematician Milutin Milankovitch refined the

concept linking ice ages with changes in the earth's attitude and its orbit around the sun to an extent that the
concept was named after him.

In 1976, two Americans and an English scientist published the strongest evidence to date that both Wegener
and Milankovitch were correct. Analyzing sediment cores
drilled from beneath the floor of the Indian Ocean, James
Hays of Columbia, John Imbrie of Brown University, and
Nicholas Shackleton of Cambridge University assembled
what they feel is a highly accurate record of the earth's
climate dating back 450,000 years. The trio then correlated the information with data about the earth's orbit.
They substantiated the theory that the timing of each of
the planet's major ice ages was closely related to changes
in the earth's attitude and orbit which reduced the
amount of summer sunlight touching the polar caps. The
scientists conclude that unless man somehow unbalances
the equation, the trend over the next 20,000 years will be
toward a cooler global climate and the spread of glaciers
in the northern hemisphere, with the inevitable ice age on
the horizon. A worldwide average temperature drop of
only 1° F would shorten growing seasons in the temperate
zones enough to threaten global food supplies.


It is well-documented that a steady buildup of carbon
dioxide in the earth's atmosphere has been occurring
ever since the industrial revolution began. This has been
caused by the burning of fossil fuels such as coal and oil.
They contribute to the so-called "greenhouse effect,"
which results from higher levels of colorless, odorless gas
that tends to warm up the earth by holding in the infrared
radiation (heat) which normally would escape into space.
Since the end of the last century the $CO_2$ level has climbed
by more than 12 percent. By 2000, earth scientists predict
it may climb an additional 25 percent, enough to trigger a
0.6 C (1° F) rise in the planet's average temperature.

| SOURCE | SULFUR OXIDES | PARTIC- ULATES | CARBON MONOXIDE | HYDRO- CARBONS | OXIDES OF NITROGEN |
|---|---|---|---|---|---|
| Transportation | 1.0 | 0.7 | 111.0 | 19.5 | 11.7 |
| Fuel combustion in stationary sources | 26.5 | 6.8 | 0.8 | 0.6 | 10.0 |
| Industrial process losses | 6.0 | 13.3 | 11.4 | 5.5 | 0.2 |
| Solid waste disposal | 0.1 | 1.4 | 7.2 | 2.0 | 0.4 |
| Agricultural burning | --- | 2.4 | 13.8 | 2.8 | 0.3 |
| Miscellaneous | 0.3 | 1.5 | 4.5 | 4.5 | 0.2 |
| TOTALS | 33.9 | 26.1 | 148.7 | 34.9 | 22.8 |

But, other climatologists and meteorologists question whether fuel particles, or all the other particles emitted by man such as smoke from industry and slash-and-burn agriculture, dust from cleared land, or exhausts from automobiles and aircraft, have the capacity to either warm the earth's atmosphere by absorption of sunlight, or cool the planet by deflecting away incoming sunlight. They point to the violent 1963 eruption of Bali's Mount Agung which shot up so much volcanic dust into the stratosphere that it measurably reduced the amount of solar radiation reaching the world's soils. But the effect was only temporary. At the time, Soviet and American earth scientists independently concluded that a permanent drop of only 1.6 to 2 percent in energy reaching the earth would cause such unstable conditions to develop as to stimulate an advance of continental snow cover toward the equator. In their opinion, the oceans would eventually freeze.

Such eminent climatologists as J. Murray Mitchell and Hubert H. Lamb, a historian of climate at England's University of East Anglia, feel that volcanic dust riding the high stratosphere may in the long distant past have triggered climatic change. Indeed, it may have pushed the earth over the fine line into the ice age which had gripped it for more than two and a half million years.

Other earth scientists see the cooling trend of the '50s and '60s leveling off and worldwide temperatures rising. For evidence, they cite the uncharacteristically mild Scandinavian winters during recent years. In Antarctica, Australia, and New Zealand, temperatures have risen sharply. Temperatures measured over some fifty stations along North America's middle latitudes have either remained fixed or risen slightly over the past few years.

To those in the eastern half of the United States gripped by the Big Freeze of 1977, the warming prospect has obvious appeal. But a global warming trend could be just as disastrous as a worldwide freeze. More than a modest rise in temperature could begin melting polar ice caps, causing extensive coastal flooding, drastically altering air circulation and rainfall patterns, and cutting the productivity of many important agricultural areas.

The consensus, however, among scientists is that whatever the reasons behind 1977's weather patterns, they cannot at this time be relegated to any of the long-range cooling—or warming—trends foreseen by a few scientists. George Kukla, a climatologist at Columbia University, argues, "Just because we can't get our cars started, are suffering from frostbite, and have a few feet of snow in our driveways, we should not start worrying about an ice age."

Obviously, only time and more research will reveal which, if either, of the warming or cooling scenarios is correct. Whatever the long-term forecast is, all scientists do concur that the earth's climate is entering a period of increased change and variability in which weather patterns are likely to fluctuate far more precipitously than during the past five decades.

## The Earth Is Changing

Within the past few years scientists have come to a startling new understanding about our shifting, shuddering, hot-hearted planet. In attempting to explain why the Atlantic widens, the Pacific narrows, the Alps grow higher, Los Angeles slides northward toward San Francisco, and Africa splits apart, they postulate the earth's crust consists of some twenty "plates" or continents drifting majestically from place to place. This new view of the earth, consisting of a crazy quilt of great rafts from thirty to one hundred miles thick, has the plates sliding over a hot, semiplastic layer below. The plates grind and crush together, causing earthquakes and volcanic eruptions. Some plates crack in the ocean basins where they are thinnest and the pieces move apart. In the cracks molten rock wells up and solidifies, like new ice forming. The edges of other plates bend downward, and slide beneath the edge of an adjacent plate forming the deep oceanic trenches or edge of a continent to be consumed within the earth's interior.

Indeed, as recently as the spring of 1977, an American expedition of geologists, geophysicists, and geochemists under sponsorship of the U.S. Academy of Sciences and the Woods Hole Oceanographic Institution in Massachusetts were probing a unique volcanic phenomenon along an undersea rift near the Galapagos Islands where the earth's crust is being pushed apart.

Ten years ago, all this would have sounded like a chapter from one of Edgar Rice Burroughs' fantasy stories. Today, however, a sweeping revolution in our understanding of the earth is taking place. In the past few years scientists have achieved new insights about the forces which shape the earth. The recent revolutionary thinking has been compared to the scientific upheavals which occurred when Copernicus demonstrated how our planet is not the center of the universe, when Darwin postulated the slow evolution of living things, and when Niels Bohr described the atom.

Scientists are now trying to understand the correlation between the changes on earth and the altered circulation of the oceans and the atmosphere, the two vast heat-carrying mechanisms of the climate machine. Surely, the rearing up and wearing down of mountains and the slow drift of continents across the earth's surface must make a difference in weather. Fifty million years ago, Antarctica and Australia were joined.

Surely the changes in land and seas since the earth formed were bound to alter world climate. Indeed, some climatologists believe that continental drift could have brought on different epochs in our evolution. Professor Edward N. Lorenz of the Massachusetts Institute of Technology feels that one tiny variation at one spot on the changing earth may have vastly multiplied effects at other spots. "Can the flap of a butterfly's wings in Peru cause a tornado in Iowa?" he asks seriously. He thinks it is possible that a random tiny disturbance to the atmosphere on one side of the globe might trigger off other disturbances, grow, and change entire weather patterns on the other side.

As sea floors spread, plates move, and the earth's rigid crust is destroyed and recreated, climatologists continue to analyze the mystery between atmospheric circulation and heat exchange between the oceans and air. Trying to measure and reduce to simple equations the vast swirls of the earth's atmosphere, and to predict from them what may happen in the future is a difficult job. It imposes upon weathermen incredible problems in the sheer magnitude of the mathematics and data handling—so complex as to be almost incomprehensible. The arrival of the electronic computer is aiding in tackling these complex problems.

In 1946, John Von Neumann, a mathematician at the Institute for Advanced Study in Princeton, New Jersey, was the first to create a "model" for weather and its prediction, eventually utilizing a computer. Thirty years later, Von Neumann's students are carrying on the work, employing the latest machines available. Labeled ASC, Advanced Scientific Computer, the new computer can handle more calculations at higher rates of speed than almost any other computer ever designed. ASC calculates the dynamics of the entire atmosphere at nine different altitude levels, as well as the circulation of the oceans.

Dr. Joseph Smogorinsky, Director of NOAA's Geophysical Fluid Dynamics Laboratory at Princeton says, "We can mathematically change the sun's intensity and see what happens to the world weather map. At the end we have a set of answers. Then we have to find out if we're even close to being right."

But so expensive and arcane is the game of simulating global climate in detail, as well as correlating the ongoing changes of the earth with atmospheric changes, that only a few of America's computing laboratories can take part in it: Princeton, UCLA, the Rand Corporation, NCAR at Boulder. All have a role in the decade-long scientific effort under the United Nations, the Global Atmospheric Research Programme (GARP), established in part to "provide greater knowledge of basic earth physical changes and forces affecting climate."

Earth scientists have learned a great deal about the changing earth and broad characteristics of climate, but their knowledge about the major processes and mechanisms of climate change remains, at best, fragmentary. Not only are the basic scientific questions largely unanswered, scientists don't understand enough to even pose the key questions. For example, what really are the most crucial causes of climatic variation? Which are the most important or most sensitive of the many processes involved during the interaction of ice, sea, land, and air? Although there is strong evidence correlating the ocean with the atmosphere, climatologists cannot yet determine the ocean's effect on climatic change. Also, there have recently been suggestions that the earth's climates may be significantly influenced by long-term astronomical variations of the sun's radiation received at the top of the atmosphere. There is no doubt whatsoever in the minds of scientists that the earth's climates have changed dramatically throughout time and will likely change in the future—but can we, with our science and technology, spot the first phases of a truly significant climate change when it begins?

Climatic changes take place on a variety of scales. These range from the change of local climate resulting from the removal of a forest to regional or global anomalies resulting from shifting patterns of large-scale circulation. Unlike the day-to-day weather, variations in climate take place very slowly over years, sometimes even decades or thousands of years. The system is complex and the search for order in the climatic record has only begun.

Today, the earth scientist's fundamental goal is to increase his understanding of climatic variations to the point of prediction and possibly control. Such a successful execution of this goal requires the help of fellow scientists from the fields of the physical sciences of meteorology, oceanography, glaciology, hydrology, astronomy, geology, and paleontology, and from the biological and social sciences of ecology, geography, archeology, history, economics, and sociology. An intensive effort of this sort requires a long-term commitment from both the scientific community and sponsoring government agencies.

# II

# Understanding Climate Change

*The one constant certainty in the world is change.*
I Ching

Clinging to this small, spinning planet's land and water surfaces is a formless and invisible mantle of air—our atmosphere. This enveloping mixture of gases, water vapor, and minute particles of solid material is a highly unstable mass, keenly sensitive to both the rays of the sun and motions of the earth. Acted upon by the combined effects of the earth's motions and solar radiation, the changing qualities of the atmosphere unite to create incredible varieties in weather. In turn, those varieties create the very fundamental patterns of the world's climates.

But exactly what is climate? And, more important, what are the physical bases for climatic change?

*Climate* is the "normal" weather condition of a particular area during a specific time period. Climatic properties are generally defined as thermal properties— including the temperature of land, water, ice, and air. This also includes kinetic properties such as the ocean currents and winds, vertical motions, and the motions of ice masses. Aqueous properties of climate include the air's moisture, or humidity, and the cloudiness and cloud water content, groundwater, lake levels, and the water content of snow, land, and sea ice. The static properties of the climatic system include the pressure and density of the ocean and atmosphere, as well as the composition of the dry air, the oceanic salinity, and the geometric boundaries and physical constants of the system. These variables are all interconnected by the constants of the system, such as rain and evaporation radiation, and the transfer of heat and momentum of turbulence.

The complete climatic system consists of five physical components: the atmosphere, hydrosphere, cryosphere, lithosphere, and biosphere.

*Atmosphere:* Comprises the earth's gaseous envelope and is the most variable part of the system. Although this gaseous envelope is a mixture of a number of gases, nitrogen (78 percent) and oxygen (21 percent) make up 99 percent of the total volume. What little remains is composed of a number of other gases. Ordinary surface air differs somewhat from this. In addition to the permanent gases, surface air contains variable amounts of water vapor and organic and inorganic impurities, including dust and condensed water and ice particles. Although the amount of water vapor in the air varies greatly from time to time and place to place, it rarely exceeds 3 percent by volume, even in the humid tropics.

We live at the bottom of the atmosphere, under a virtual ocean of air. Extending upward perhaps 1,000 miles, this massive, restless ocean is far different and far more tempestuous than the watery oceans which cover three-fourths of the earth's surface.

A narrow band of compacted air lying just above the earth is the region of continuous winds. Here, the rising

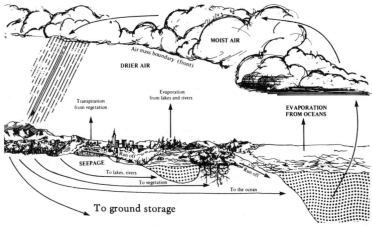

MOIST AIR

Air mass boundary (front)

DRIER AIR

Evaporation
from lakes and rivers

Transpiration
from vegetation

EVAPORATION
FROM OCEANS

SEEPAGE

Run off

To lakes, rivers

To vegetation

Run off

To the ocean

To ground storage

The hydrologic cycle.

and falling air currents sometimes develop into violent storms. Only recently have the most advanced aircraft ventured above this thin layer, some six to twelve miles thick. Interestingly, the air in the atmospheric ocean is highly compressible: a cubic foot of air at the surface weighs billions of times as much as a cubic foot at the outer edge of the atmosphere. The atmosphere thins so rapidly as one leaves the earth that only 3½ miles, up over 50 percent of the atmosphere by weight would lie below you. It is chiefly in this 3½-mile blanket of heavy air that weather changes are born and created. The atmosphere 500 miles away from earth is so thin that there are only about 22 million molecules of air per cubic inch compared to billions upon billions of molecules per cubic inch at the earth's surface. Still farther out, the ever-thinning atmosphere blends with the stray gases and dust of outer space.

Thus, the atmosphere is the most variable part of the system and has a characteristic response or thermal adjustment time on the order of a month. This simply means that the atmosphere, by transferring heat vertically and horizontally, will adjust itself to an imposed temperature change in about thirty days. This is also approximately the time it would take for the atmosphere's kinetic energy to be dissipated by friction, if there were no processes acting to replenish the energy.

*Hydrosphere:* Encompasses all the water spread over the surface of the earth. This includes the oceans, lakes, rivers, and all the water beneath the earth's surface, such as subterranean and ground water. Of all this, the earth's oceans are the most significant for climatic variations. Since the oceans absorb most of the solar radiation that touches the earth's surface, the oceanic temperature structure represents an enormous reservoir of energy, due to its large mass and heat. The upper layers of the ocean interact with the overlying atmosphere on time scales of months to years, while the deeper ocean waters have thermal adjustment times on the order of centuries.

As far as the hydrologic cycle is concerned, scientists say that during the last four billion years since the origin of the earth, water environments have been in motion. The waters of all geologic history are still the waters of the 20th century. Little has been added or lost through the ages since the original clouds formed and the first rains fell. The same water has been transferred time and time again from the oceans into the atmosphere, dropped upon the land, and transferred back to the sea.

Distribution of Land and Water on the Earth's Surface

| HEMISPHERE | LAND (percent) | OCEAN (percent) |
|---|---|---|
| Northern | 39.3 | 60.7 |
| Southern | 19.1 | 80.9 |

This hydrologic cycle is a natural machine, a constantly running distillation and pumping system. The sun supplies heat energy and this together with the force of gravity keeps the water moving, from the earth to the atmosphere as evaporation and transpiration, from the atmosphere to the earth as condensation and precipitation, and between points on the earth as stream-flow and ground-water movement. As a hydrologic cycle, this system of water has neither beginning nor end.

Cryosphere: Comprises the world's ice masses and snow deposits, including the continental ice sheets, mountain glaciers, sea ice, surface snow cover, and lake and river ice. The changes of snow cover on the land are primarily seasonal and closely tied to the atmospheric circulation. The glaciers and ice sheets (which house the bulk of the world's freshwater storage) respond to changes in

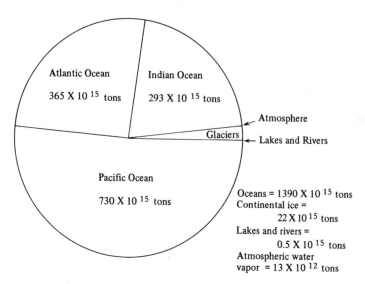

Mass of free water (in tons) on the earth's surface. Note the minute fraction of the total that occurs as fresh water (lakes and rivers) at any instant.

climatic conditions much more slowly. Because of their huge mass, these systems develop dynamics of their own, and they display significant changes in both volume and extent over periods ranging from hundreds to millions of years. Such variations are naturally and closely related to the global hydrologic balance and to variations of sea level.

Of all the forms of ice masses and snow deposits, none is more important to global weather patterns, or a potential water resource for drought-stricken areas than the glacier. Yet, most people have never seen a glacier. Most Americans would say that glaciers are rare features found only in inaccessible arctic areas. But about three fourths of all the fresh water in the world (equivalent to about eighty years' rain over the entire globe) is now stored as glacier ice. In North America, the volume of water stored as snow and ice in glaciers is many times greater than that stored in all of the lakes, ponds, rivers, and reservoirs on the continent. In some states, such as Alaska, Washington, Montana, and Idaho, glaciers are an important supply of dry-season water, and regulate naturally the streamflow to even out the seasonal and year-to-year variations in rain.

In the United States, today, there are some 1,100 glaciers, covering a total area of 205 square miles. Most are tiny cirques (glaciers found in protected amphitheaters carved out of mountain slopes by the ice itself). The total July-August streamflow derived from these glaciers in an average year is equivalent to about 600 billion gallons of water for the two months. About 3 percent of Alaska's 17,000 square miles is covered by glaciers and most of that state's rivers originate from them. The peculiar characteristics of glacier runoff (peak flows during mid-summer, distinct day-to-night differences in runoff, large silt content of stream water and occasional outburst floods) play an important role in Alaska's climatic change.

The melting of snow and ice does not necessarily depend upon the warmth of the air. The rate of melt depends more on the heat balance at the snow or ice surface. Heat is gained by radiation from the sun and from warm clouds, from warm air, and from the condensation of dew. The sun's radiation is usually the most important source of heat. Heat is lost by radiation out to space, by evaporation, and by the energy which goes into ice melt. If the winter's snowpack is very heavy, the coating of highly reflective snow persists for an extended time over a large area during the summer. This in turn causes more solar radiation to be reflected and less to be absorbed than during a normal year. The more snowfall, the less runoff there is. The converse is also true: the less rain or snow there is, the more runoff occurs. The melting produces a remarkable natural regulation of glacier runoff from year to year.

Currently, the Soviet Union and China are experimenting with the artificial regulation of glacier streamflow in order to determine its effect on the region's climatic changes. Whenever water in the form of ice is added to storage, glaciers grow and advance and the runoff is less than the precipitation. Whenever glaciers retreat, water is released from storage and runoff exceeds precipitation. The effect of this long-term storage and release of water can be appreciable. But thus far, no one knows its effect on the climate.

Lithosphere: This includes the land masses covering the surface of the earth, including the mountains and ocean basins, along with soil, sediments, and surface rock. Land masses and other features, such as mountains, erode over the longest time scale of all the components of the climatic system, dating all the way back to the birth of the earth itself. Earth scientists now know that the processes of continental drift and sea-floor spreading which have created mountain ranges and changed the shapes and

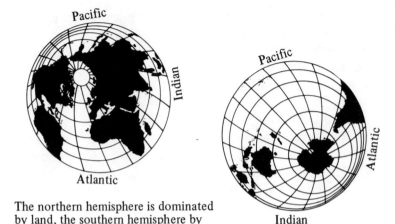

The northern hemisphere is dominated
by land, the southern hemisphere by
water.

depths of ocean floors have occurred over billions of
years.

*Biosphere:* Comprises all the plant cover on the planet's
land and ocean, as well as all living creatures. Although
man, animals, and reptiles respond differently, each life
form is sensitive to climate and in turn may actually influence climatic change. From this biosphere, scientists
obtain most of their data on ancient climates. The natural
changes in surface vegetation triggered by changes in
temperature and rain alter surface chemistry, evaporation, and ground hydrology. These changes may take
place over decades or over thousands of years. Changes
in animal population also reflect climatic variations
because of the availability of suitable food and habitat.
Scientists now conclude that the impact of man on nature
and changes due to agriculture and animal husbandry
are at best little understood, but may well be appreciable
in altering at least regional climates.

The climate at any one time, then, represents in some
sense the average of the various kinds of elements of

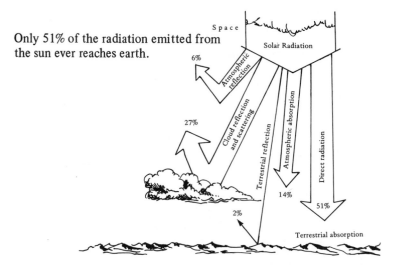

Only 51% of the radiation emitted from the sun ever reaches earth.

weather, along with the particular state of the other components of the system. The actual physical processes responsible for climate (differing from climatic change) are therefore very similar to those responsible for weather.

The most important factor in the circulation of the atmosphere and ocean is where heat is added to the system and the rate at which it is added. The most important source of heat is the sun's radiation. The atmosphere and ocean respond to this heating by developing winds and currents, which in turn carry heat from those regions where it is received in abundance (equatorial and tropical areas) to areas where almost no radiation (heat) is received (the polar regions). In this manner, the atmosphere and ocean maintain the overall global balance of heat. A major portion of this heat is transported by the winds, storms, and disturbances responsible for much of the earth's weather.

Many other far more subtle physical processes are affecting climatic change. The heating rate is itself highly dependent upon the distribution of the temperature and moisture in the atmosphere and owes much to the release of latent heat during the formation of clouds. Clouds subsequently influence solar and terrestrial radiation. These processes, coupled with others that contribute to the overall heat balance of the atmosphere are shown below. The presence of clouds, water vapor, and $CO_2$ blocks over 90 percent of the radiation emitted by the earth's surface (the greenhouse effect) and permits a somewhat higher surface temperature than otherwise might be the case. It is interesting that the crucial effect of warming the earth is achieved by gases in the atmosphere which exist in near trace amounts.

In the figure, it can be seen how important a role is played by clouds. The reflection and emission from clouds accounts for approximately 46 percent of the total radiation leaving the atmosphere. In terms of shortwave radiation alone, clouds account for two-thirds of the planetary reflective power.

Cumulonimbus clouds: Huge masses of clouds with high vertical development (up to 60,000 feet). The true cumulonimbus have a layer on top which is composed of ice crystals. These, then, are the true thunderstorm clouds which can result in rain and hail.

Stratocumulus clouds: Irregular masses spread out in an undulating or puffy layer. These formations are most often seen in winter. They generally are low (750 feet) and fairly thick (1,250 feet).

Cirrocumulus clouds: Generally form between 15,000 and 20,000 feet and are composed almost entirely of ice crystals. They are a transient formation, often forming from either cirrus or cirrostratus, and then quickly returning to their original form. Their wave-like pattern resembles the backs of fish.

Nimbostratus clouds:  Low, dark-gray clouds which are the true rain clouds.  They will generally produce steady rain.  The cloud bases are usually 1,500 feet above the ground.

Stratus clouds:  Generally form a low uniform layer which appears like fog, although they do not rest on the ground.  Cloud bases range from near the ground up to approximately 7,000 feet.  Drizzle is generally the only kind of precipitation emitted.

Cumulus clouds: Heavy, thick, white puffy clouds. Their tops are rounded, while their bases are flat. These clouds rarely produce rain, but often form into cumulonimbus clouds, which do produce rain.

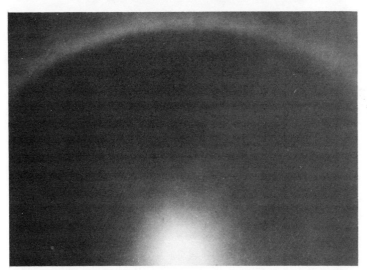

Cirrostratus clouds: Form at 15,000 to 23,000 feet and form thin sheets which look like veils. Because of their ice crystal composition and broad extent, they form halos around the sun and moon.

Cirrus clouds: Wispy, feathery, and extremely thin. They usually form above 25,000 feet where the temperature is well below freezing. They consist almost entirely of ice crystals. Frequently, cirrus clouds are blown into feather-like strands.

Altostratus clouds: Consist of liquid water droplets. They form between 1,500 to 2,500 feet thick and have their base around 13,000 feet, and appear as dense veils or sheets of gray or blue. Altostratus clouds veil out the sun, giving the impression of a watery sky. These clouds, however, contain no precipitation.

Altocumulus clouds: Have their bases above 10,000 feet and appear as large globular masses of gray and white. They are arranged in groups or lines with their edges often indistinct. Cumulus clouds generally precede altocumulus clouds. Considerable vertical development, but no layer of ice crystals.

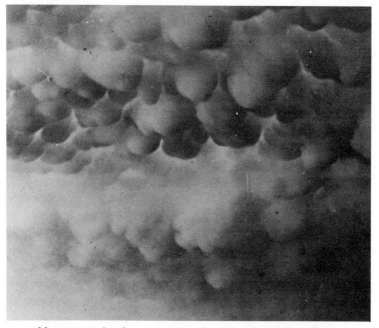

Mammatus clouds: Are series of pouches projecting downward from the base of storm clouds. These pouches are usually uniform in size and shape, appear and flatten gradually, and have no spinning motion. These are the kinds of clouds which are often associated with tornadoes. If you see such clouds, seek shelter.

### How Weather Comes About

It might be useful at this point to introduce a number of concepts and definitions related to weather and climatic change. In the simplest of definitions, *weather* is the state created by the atmosphere in terms of heat or cold, dryness or wetness, calmness or disturbance, clear or overcast. *Climate,* on the other hand, is the average of the various weather elements, taken over a particular period, usually thirty years. All weather changes are formed by temperature changes in different segments of the atmosphere. Of course, the source of virtually all the earth's heat is the sun, that incredible ball of glowing gases some 93 million miles away. That massive, atomic-generated furnace bombards small, fragile earth with over 130 trillion horsepower every second. Yet, according to scientists, this gigantic energy is but a half of one billionth of the sun's total output each second! Virtually all that solar energy is diffused into deep space. As far as the earth is concerned, the energy arrives as waves, similar to radio waves. Some are invisible, while others

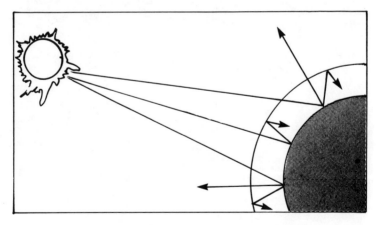

A greenhouse "traps" solar radiation when
"short" solar rays change to "long" heat rays.

are seen as light waves. Some of the waves transform into heat when absorbed by living matter and other objects. Scientists say that 43 percent of the radiation reaching the earth's surface is changed to heat.

When scientists speak of the "greenhouse effect" on earth, what they mean in essence is that the "glass" of a greenhouse allows the short solar rays to pass through. These rays are absorbed by objects inside which then re-radiate as long heat rays. But re-radiated rays cannot penetrate the "glass." Thus, the heat rays are continually re-absorbed and re-radiated inside.

While all this is occurring, the atmosphere is serving as a thermostat and filter. Protecting the planet from too much solar radiation during the day, it not only screens the dangerous rays, but also serves as an insulating blanket which prevents most of the heat from leaving at night. Without its thick and heavy atmosphere, the earth would have temperatures like the moon's—240° F below zero to 212° F.

When air is warmed, it expands and becomes lighter. Warmed by contact with the earth, this layer of air rises and is replaced by colder air which flows in and under it. In turn, this cold air is heated and rises. Then, it, too, is replaced by colder air. Such a circulating movement of warm and cold fluids is called *convection*.

Since the air at the equator receives much more heat than the air at the poles, the warm air at the equator rises and is replaced by colder air flowing in from both the north and south. The light, warm air rises and moves poleward high above the earth. As it cools, it drops, replacing the cool surface air which has moved toward the equator.

Convection causes local winds and breezes. Different land and water surfaces absorb different amounts of heat. Plowed, dark soil absorbs much more than grassy fields. Mountains and hills absorb heat faster during

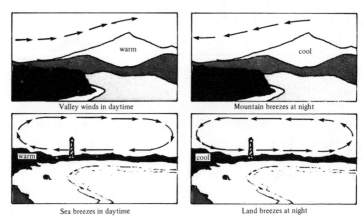

| | |
|---|---|
| Valley winds in daytime | Mountain breezes at night |
| Sea breezes in daytime | Land breezes at night |

Differences in heating cause local winds.

daylight than nearby valleys, and lose it faster at night. Land warms faster than does water during the day and cools more rapidly at night. Thus, the air above such surfaces is warmed or cooled accordingly, resulting in local winds.

Heat and atmospheric water are the two key ingredients of rain and snow. The eternal process of evaporation, condensation, and rain begins when heat evaporates millions of tons of water in the air every day. Lakes, streams, and oceans send up a steady stream of water vapor. Water is also transpired from all green plants. Surprisingly, a single apple tree may move 1,800 gallons of water into the air in a single six-month growing season.

As moist, warm air rises, it slowly cools so much that its relative humidity reaches 100 percent. *Humidity* is the amount of water vapor in the air, while *relative humidity* is the amount of vapor the air contains expressed as a percentage of the amount the air can hold at that particular temperature. Warm air can hold more water than cold. When air with a given amount of water vapor cools, its relative humidity goes up. When the air is warmed, its relative humidity drops. During the final phase of the

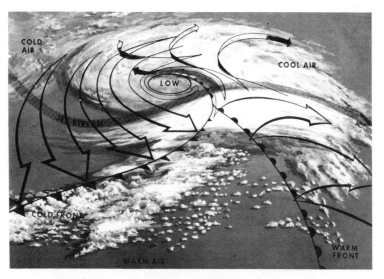

This illustration shows a typical front as seen from above. A warm front is at the lower right, cold air in the upper left. Arrows show the wind directions.

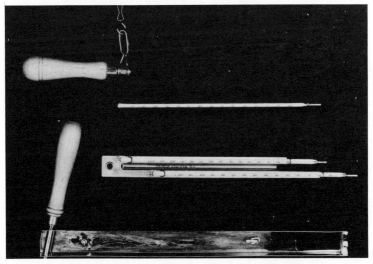

A sling psychrometer is used to measure relative humidity. It consists of two thermometers: a mercury thermometer and a thermometer with a moistened muslin wick over its bulb. Evaporation from the wick lowers the temperature of the thermometer.

water cycle, clouds form and under certain conditions, rain, snow and hail is pulled down by the earth's gravity.

To understand climatic change, it is useful to define *climatic state, variation, anomaly*, and *variability*.

*Climatic state* is the average of atmospheric, hydrospheric, and cryospheric characteristics over a specified period of time in a designated area. Scientists refer to monthly, seasonal, yearly, or decadal climatic states.

*Climatic variation* is the difference between similar climatic states, between two Januaries, or even between two decades. Scientists refer to monthly, seasonal, yearly, or decadal climatic variations; the term "climatic change" is often used interchangeably with climatic variation.

*Climatic anomaly* is a deviation from the average climatic state. Thus, climatic anomaly can be represented by a particular month or by a particular year.

*Climatic variability* is the variance among a number of similar climatic states. Climatologists refer to monthly, seasonal, yearly or decadal climatic variability.

### Why Climates Change

When it comes to describing the processes responsible for the continuation of a particular climate in a certain area, scientists have little trouble, but coming up with a description of the processes involved in climatic change is another matter. He has to consider a wide range of possible interactions among the elements of the climatic system. It is precisely these interactions which are responsible for the complexity of climatic variation.

For example, changes in solar radiation distribution have been used for decades to explain the major glacial

SUMMER TEMPERATURE

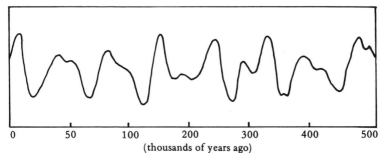

| 0 | 50 | 100 | 200 | 300 | 400 | 500 |

(thousands of years ago)

Summer temperatures have varied from cool to warm
over the past 500,000 years. The cycle repeats itself
about every 21,000 years.

cycles. Besides variations in the sun's radiative output,
variations in the earth's orbit also produce changes in the
intensity and geographical pattern of the seasonal and
annual radiation and in the length of the radiational
seasons in each hemisphere. These variations, scientists
feel, have resulted in occasional variations much larger
than anything experienced now. These orbital elements
vary with periods averaging approximately 96,000 years,
41,000 years, and 21,000 years, respectively. Because the
seasons themselves represent substantial climatic variations, such astronomical theories of climatic change are
given careful consideration.

Other concepts and theories for climatic change are offered in a committee report entitled "Understanding
Climatic Change: A Program for Action," published by the
National Academy of Sciences. For instance, the separate
question of the climatic effects of possible changes in the
radiation of the sun itself is weighed. Such changes in the
so-called solar constant has a much less firm physical
basis. The measured short-period variations of solar output have proven quite insignificant, and the repeated
search for climatic changes linked with the 11-year and
80-year sunspot cycles has not yielded statistically con-
clusive results. The question of still longer-period solar

variations, concludes the committee, cannot be adequately examined with present knowledge, even though over hundreds of millions of years the sun's radiation seems likely to have changed.

In terms of tens of millions of years, there have been significant changes in the shapes of the ocean basins and the distribution of continents as a result of continent drift and the spreading of sea floors. Over such long periods of time, geological processes must have resulted in major world climate changes. Exactly how many changes, and to what degree they occurred, remain a mystery. Conceiving and applying climatic models to the systematic reconstruction of the earth's climatic history before 15 million years ago is one of the several recommendations the committee has made.

Another external reason for climatic variation is the changes in the composition of the atmosphere taking place due to the natural chemical evolution of the nitrogen, oxygen, and carbon dioxide content because of geological and biological processes.

In terms of shorter periods of time, it has probably been the shooting of volcanic dust particles into the atmosphere that has accounted for the more significant climatic variations. Such volcanic dust can modify the atmospheric radiation balance. Also, the continued pollution of the atmosphere due to the combustion of fossil fuels (an increase of 10 percent since the 1880s) is also a chief external cause of climatic variation.

Variations in the global ice distribution have also had a major impact on the total heating capacity of the atmosphere, since variations may change the heating conditions which trigger oceanic and atmospheric circulation. An equally important change for the oceans may occur because of widespread salinity variations caused by melting ice.

Such natural and complex processes may act as internal controls of the climatic system over time scales ex-

This aerovane transmitter is like a small airplane
without wings. The nose turns into the wind,
slowing wind direction, and the whirling propellor
gives wind speed in miles per hour. The 3-cup
anemometer (lower right) measures wind speed.

Weather station mercurial barometers are precision-
made and accurate to 1/1000 inch. They respond
to changes in temperature as well as pressure because
the mercury column itself expands with heat.

tending from months to thousands of years. A few of these intricate processes show a "coupling," or mutual compensation effect among two or more elements within the internal climatic system. Such interacting mechanisms may either exaggerate or reduce the effect of the elements. Coupling between cloudiness and surface temperature will result in an initial increase of surface temperature and thereby increase evaporation. This in turn is followed by an increase in cloudiness, which diminishes solar radiation reaching the surface and therefore lowers the initial temperature.

In short periods of climatic change, especially those concerning radiation balance over land and the energy balance over the ocean, ocean surface temperature may alter the transfer of heat to the overlying atmosphere and thereby affect circulation and cloudiness. Ocean surface temperatures are affected by the sun's radiation, wind mixing, the horizontal movement of air over the water, and the converging of two different currents or flows. These processes result in the enhancement or reduction of sea surface temperature. A number of research projects have demonstrated these processes over several years' time in the north Pacific.

Perhaps the greenhouse effect is the best demonstration of a temporary feedback process. For example, an increase of snow extent will increase the surface cover of the land and thereby lower the surface temperature. All else being normal, this will in turn further increase the extent of the snow cover.

To earth scientists, the problem of isolating the causes of climatic change would be much simplified if all else were equal. In our highly complex climate system, this is generally not the situation. An aberration in one part of the system will often trigger a whole series of compensations, or adjustments, depending upon the type, location, and magnitude of the disturbance. Scientists do not fully understand the adjustment mechanisms. Sys-

Launching a meteorological balloon. These weather balloons carry small instrument packages called radiosondes, and measure temperature, pressure, humidity and winds up to an elevation of 90,000 feet.

tematic studies of climate theories and models are important tasks for the future.

## Oceans and Climatic Change

There is little question that oceans play a dominant role in determining climate. The atmosphere drives the great ocean circulations and strongly affects the properties of seawater. To a great extent the atmosphere, in turn, owes its nature to and derives its energy from the ocean. The processes that occur when air touches sea are crucial since they govern the exchanges of heat, moisture, and momentum. While the processes are actually determined mutually by the ocean and the atmosphere, the ocean probably has the edge in dominance on at least the longer periods of climatic change.

In the physical process of the ocean's role in climatic change, it should be remembered that over half of the sun's radiation reaching the earth's surface is absorbed by the water. That solar radiation, coupled with the surface wind stress is the most important energy source for the variety of physical processes which take place in the ocean. The absorption of solar radiation is primarily responsible for the existence of a warm surface layer 100 meters deep found over most of the world's seas and oceans. That warm surface layer represents a huge reservoir of heat and acts as an important heat constraint upon atmospheric circulation.

Taking place over a wide range of time scales, the exchange of the ocean's heat with the atmosphere determines the relative significance of other physical processes in the ocean for climatic change. For instance, some of this heat is used for surface evaporation, some is stored in the surface layer, and some is moved downward into much deeper water by various processes.

According to R. W. Stewart, eminent physicist and chairman of the Physical Oceanographic Commission, "The dynamics of the ocean's surface layer must be taken into account in even the simplest of climate models."

The ocean's great effect on climate can be understood by comparing the climate of coastal areas to that of inland areas. Near oceans, the climate is generally slightly warmer and more moderate, showing significantly smaller variations and swings in temperature.

Automatic observation instrumentation

Wind direction

Temperature dewpoint        Precipitation accumulation

AMOS III-70

Precipitation occurence

For example, Victoria, Canada, is a part of the southern tip of Vancouver Island, on the eastern shore of the Pacific. Winnipeg is located in the middle of the North American land mass, and St. John's is on the island of Newfoundland, protruding into the western Atlantic. The most striking climatic difference among the three is the enormous temperature range at Winnipeg compared to the two coastal cities. The range at St. John's, although much smaller, is still greater than at Victoria, primarily because at St. John's, the air usually blows from the direction of the continent and the effect of the water is somewhat less dominant than at Victoria, which receives its air directly from the ocean. St. John's is also surrounded by the cold water of the Labrador current.

|                        | VICTORIA | WINNIPEG | ST. JOHN'S |
|------------------------|----------|----------|------------|
| MEAN JULY MAXIMUM      | 68       | 80.1     | 68.9       |
| MEAN JANUARY MINIMUM   | 35.6     | −8.1     | 18.5       |

Compared to the land, the ocean heats slowly in summer and cools slowly in winter, so that its temperature is much less variable. Because air has so much less thermal capacity, when it blows over water it tends to become water temperature rather than vice versa. For these reasons, maritime climates are much more moderate than continental climates.

Although the ocean affects the atmosphere's temperature more than the atmosphere affects the ocean's, the ocean is cooled when it gives up heat to the atmosphere. According to Dr. Stewart:

> The density of ocean water is controlled by two factors, temperature and salinity, and evaporative cooling tends to make the water denser by affecting both factors: it lowers the temperature and, since evaporation removes water but comparatively little salt, it also increases the salinity. If surface water becomes denser

than the water underlying it, vigorous vertical convective mixing sets in. In a few places in the ocean, the
cooling at the surface can be so intense that the water
will sink and mix to great depths, sometimes right to
the bottom. Such occurrences are rare both in space
and in time, but once cold water has reached great
depths it is heated from above very slowly, and so tends
to stay deep for a long time with little change in
temperature; there is some evidence of water that has
remained cold and deep in the ocean for more than
1,000 years.

Earth scientists agree that it is not enough to imply that
the atmosphere drives the ocean and that heat supplied
from the ocean is largely instrumental in releasing energy
for the atmosphere. Accurate oceanic circulation models
must be constructed to augment similarly accurate and
compatible atmospheric models. Because there is a great
deal of feedback between the two systems, the atmospheric patterns determine the oceanic flows, which in
turn influence where and how much heat is released to
the atmosphere. In turn, the atmospheric flow systems
determine how much cloud cover there will be over certain parts of the ocean and therefore how much and
where the ocean will be heated.

Of particular importance for climate change studies
is the need to construct accurate models of the oceanic
surface mixed layer, since all the physical processes in
the ocean ultimately exert their influence on the atmosphere through the surface of the sea. Until the dynamics
of this oceanic boundary layer are better understood,
man's ability to model climatic variations on any time
scale will remain seriously limited.

## Past Climatic Variations

There is no question that global climate has undergone
significant variations over a wide variety of time scales
and such variations will continue in the future. Historical
records contain a great deal of information relating to

climate change which could aid the scientist's ability to forecast future variations, even on time scales as short as one or two decades. Data on crop yields, droughts, and winter severity from manuscripts, recorded explorations, and other sources provide the only available information on the general character of the climate of the past. This information is especially useful in conjunction with selected tree ring, ice core, and lake sediment data in diagnostic studies of longer-term climatic changes.

All of human civilization has occurred within one particular calm period in climatic history of some 10,000 years. Each climatic epoch has left evidence of its presence and now scientists are at work attempting to unravel the future by reconstructing the past.

During the past hundred million years, about a tenth of the earth's age, there have been at least four times when ice covered major portions of the globe. Human beings evolved after the last ice age.

As far as historical geologists can tell, extensive ice sheets also may have covered most of the earth's land area 600 million years ago during the geologic era known as the Precambrian. Almost nothing is known of that time, and even less is understood of earlier periods, since the clues have been washed clean by more recent ice sheets, as well as by the changes in the positions and topography of the drifting continents themselves.

During the long warm spells which followed each ice age, warm shallow seas and lush swamps covered most of the land's surface. But even these spells were unexplainedly interrupted every 250 million years or so by bitter cold and huge invasions of ice. At that time, the coal and oil deposits we mine and use today were laid down. Dinosaurs roamed the earth during the last warm stretch and breadfruit trees developed in Iceland.

Then, as long as 60 million years ago, the earth began cooling off and the huge ice sheet coverings returned. By two million years ago, the prehistoric ancestors of contemporary man were in the full reign of what has been termed the Pleistocene epoch. Except for fairly short periods of warming every 100,000 years or so, lasting on an average of only 10,000 years, the ice sheets have ruled the planet's climate ever since.

During the past million years alone, ice may have blanketed Europe and North America at least ten times. Each massive buildup and retreat required tens of thousands of years to occur. A few scientists, however, speculate that the climatic shifts which triggered those ponderous changes may have developed surprisingly fast, perhaps in only a few centuries. For instance, one drop from fairly warm times into a full ice age took place in Greenland 90,000 years ago in less than one hundred years. As weather turned colder, winter snow did not entirely melt away in cooler summers. New snow then fell on the old, and glaciers and ice sheets were born. Ice began spreading into lower latitudes and downward from the mountain slopes and valley.

At its greatest extent, the last such ice advance, about 20,000 years ago, spread across the north central United States, northern Europe and to a lesser degree, northwestern Siberia. Over a mile thick, it slowly and relentlessly pushed south, sculpting out the Great Lake basins, leveling mountains and hills, lifting and carrying huge boulders, and grinding up all the terrain before it. Eventually, the ice sheet blanketed virtually all of Canada and Washington, Montana, Nebraska, Illinois, Indiana, Ohio, Pennsylvania, and New Jersey. Long Island and Cape Cod are nothing more than piles of glacial debris left behind when the ice withdrew. While that retreat began some 18,000 years ago, it has only been some 8,000 years since the last of the Scandinavian peninsula ice sheet melted, and only 6,000 years since it disappeared from the northern Canadian mainland. Today, both regions are still rebounding from release of the weight, rising as much as eight inches a year in some places.

Prior to the 19th century, observant Swiss concluded that the glaciers in the Alps had formerly been much larger and had extended much farther down the mountain valleys. They noticed that the existing glaciers were slowly transporting and depositing boulders down valley, and concluded correctly that the boulders strewn about their pastures had been transported and deposited in the same exact manner centuries before. They also observed that the polished and scratched or finely grooved and rounded bedrock knobs along the valley walls and floors were similar to those emerging from beneath the melting ice of the existing glaciers. The similarity suggested that the bedrock knobs had been produced by the moving glacial ice at a time when the glaciers were larger and extended farther down the valleys.

This observation was enlarged and popularized by the eminent Swiss geologist, Louis Agassiz. His arrival in America in 1846 marked the real beginning of the study of this fascinating period of earth history in North America. Since that time, many significant contributions to the understanding of glaciations have been made.

For example, studies proved that where great river valleys such as the Mississippi and Ohio were overwhelmed by the ice sheets, rivers were forced into new channels. Where smaller preglacial drainage systems were completely covered by glacial ice, they were commonly obliterated. Glacial deposits remaining after disappearance of the ice were usually poorly drained. Bogs, swamps, and many lakes, typical of parts of Wisconsin and Minnesota, characterize such areas.

Also, more than a hundred years ago, the intimate relationship between glacial ice and the amount of water in the ocean basins was recognized. When the great ice sheet blanketed vast areas of land, the sea level was lowered because the normal return of water from the land to the oceans was reduced. Conversely, sea level rose as ice age glaciers melted, permitting the melted waters to flow into the ocean. If all the glacial ice on the surface of the earth today should melt, sea level might rise by more than 150 feet.

Shoreline fluctuations are also produced through elevation or depression of the land. During times of glaciation, the great weight of the ice slowly depressed the earth's yielding crust. Removal of the weight through glacier melting permitted the slow rebound of the crust to its former position of relative equilibrium. Such movement, common in glaciated areas, is best illustrated in Finland and Scandinavia. Evidence of similar uplift can be seen in the region of the Great Lakes and Lake Champlain, where old shorelines (which were originally flat) are now raised and tilted so that the greatest uplift is to the north.

Fluctuations of the ice age climates from cool and wet to warm and dry produced marked environmental changes far from the glaciated areas. For instance, at times of cool-wet glacial climates, levels of inland lakes rose in contrast to the depression of sea level. During the warm-day interglacial climates, lake levels were lowered; ancient Lake Bonneville, the largest of the many glacial lakes in the western part of the United States, once extended more than 25,000 square miles and had a depth of more than 1,500 feet. The Great Salt Lake in Utah is all that is left of this once enormous lake.

Although the arrival of early man is shrouded in obscurity, he is without question a product of the great ice age. During this time, he evolved rapidly both physically and culturally. His most primitive tools and skeletal remains have been recovered from some of the oldest deposits contemporary with the great ice age in Africa, Asia, and Europe. With the eventual disappearance of the great ice sheets, the bronze and iron age cultures evolved. During this time, animals suited to cooler climates became extinct, especially larger mammals such as the woolly mammoth, mastodon, dire wolf, and saber-toothed tiger.

Although a great deal remains to be learned, the mystery of the great ice age is being unfolded. Accumulating field observations, and new theories are being offered. The great ice age is the most fascinating since it is the time of man's spectacular development, of drastic changes in climate, sea level, plant and animal life, and of the great glacial ice sheets whose frequent covering of the earth created marked changes in its character. Certainly our present environment has been greatly influenced by all these events of the great ice age.

But what really triggered these unusually long stretches of cold? What changed in the ocean, atmosphere, and climate to bring on the enormous ice sheets? Is the cause some sort of mysterious cosmic time pulse? Why, then, did one begin only 100,000 years ago?

Earth scientists say they simply do not know, although they are willing to theorize. Less than 10 years ago, two Lamont oceanographers, David Ericson and Goesta Wollin, wrote wryly, "It has been estimated that a new theory to explain continental glaciations has been published for every year that has passed since the first recognition of the evidence for past glaciation." And to Kipling's, "There are nine and sixty ways, of constructing tribal lays, and every single one of them is right," the eminent British climatologist C. E. P. Brooks added "There are, and always have been, at least nine and sixty ways of constructing a theory of climate change . . ."

Thus, in the brief span of man's written history, a mere fraction of a second in geological terms, the climate has changed and continues to change. During the so-called "climatic optimum" which started about 9,000 years ago, the average temperature in the northern hemisphere ranged two degrees higher than it does today.

From the Nile Valley to the Persian Gulf, man learned to farm, write, tame animals, and live sociably in communities. The climate was warm and men built their first great civilizations, the Egyptian and Sumerian.

From 3,000 to 2,000 B.C., very dry conditions prevailed in the ancient world. For example, the once-lush regions of North Africa and Arabia turned to desert. The Semitic peoples were driven from the Arabian peninsula into the Levant. Long droughts eventually destroyed the highly advanced Harappan civilization of the Indus Valley. The people of a once-damp and rainy Sahara disappeared into hot dust.

Cooler, wetter, stormier decades returned after 2,000 B.C. and again a thousand years later. During these years, Hittites overran Asia Minor, Medes swept into Assyria, Aryans flooded India, and during the days of Ulysses, Dorians conquered Greece. These rainy and cold decades gradually turned into warm and dry years again. Both Greece and Rome realized their golden ages between 500 B.C. and A.D. 400.

But droughts also returned. Crops in North Africa failed while grass and forests died from the Galilee to Lebanon. At the time barbarians were sacking Rome, the climate again turned colder and more wet. Europe fell into the Dark Ages. When the climate became warmer around A.D. 900, the Vikings of Scandinavia broke loose to terrorize Europe. They sailed the North Atlantic to establish colonies in North America, Greenland, and Iceland. Wine grapes were cultivated in Scotland, farther north than at any time.

But cold and wet weather returned by A.D. 1300. Pack ice lapped over Iceland and the Greenland colonies. Starving, the Greenlanders had all died by the late 1300s. Cold summers ruined European grain crops and brought about terrible famine in 1315 and 1316. During 1422-24, the Baltic Sea froze over solidly.

From those years until the mid-1800s, what is refer-
red to as a "little ice age" occurred. In the northern
hemisphere, it was much colder than it had been since the
great ice age withdrew. Famine, plague, and peasant
revolt shook Europe. Meanwhile, during the American
Revolution, heavy cannons were dragged across river ice
to Staten Island. From New England to the Carolinas,
newspapers called 1816 the "Year Without a Summer"
or "Eighteen Hundred and Froze to Death." Extra-heavy
snows fell and froze crops in Pennsylvania during July
and August.

Climatologists say that this was not all without
reason: during the year before, the Tambora volcano on
the island of Sumbawa in the East Indies exploded in one
of the greatest eruptions known in historic times.
Estimates of the amount of debris and dust thrown into
the atmosphere range from 7 to 50 cubic miles. Sunset
skies turned red around the globe by that fall. In the Alps,
the average temperature dropped by 3° F.

The climatic trend once again changed by the 1850s.
The northern temperature zone grew increasingly
warmer. Actually, the century between 1877 and 1977 is
regarded as one of the warmest since the "climatic optimum" ended some 4,000 years ago. During 1877-1977,
the Industrial Age boomed and world population more
than tripled. Farming and fishing expanded to keep pace
with food needs. Canada's wheat line inched a hundred
miles north. But this period of climate, which our great-
grandfathers and grandfathers looked upon as normal, is
now considered by earth scientists to have really been abnormally warm.

# III

# Effects of Climate Change
# on Food and Health

Ample food for the world's populations depends upon the moods of climate. The future of an expanding world population hangs in the balance. For example, in 1973, a Wisconsin farmer was able to cultivate luxuriant fields of corn as rain clouds naturally watered crops in nearby fields. Less than four years later, the once flourishing soils had turned parched in one of the midwestern states struck by severe drought. Cloud seeding attempts to provoke rain were made with silver iodide crystals in hopes that moisture would coalesce around them into raindrops. Results were totally inadequate and once again man remained at the mercy of nature.

Does the decreased rainfall actually mean a temporary dip into a dry decade? Or, is America's breadbasket really being affected by a major climatic change which would create more dust storms like the ones which plagued the area during the 1930s, and those which enveloped Cedar Rapids, Iowa, in the spring of 1976? If the earth has been cooling, as some scientists theorize, the circumpolar vortex may be gushing cold, blizzard-type air farther south, thereby blocking the usual flow of warm, moisture-laden tropical air. If this proves to be the case, such a shift means shorter growing seasons all around the northern hemisphere.

Climatologists feel that an annual temperature shift from 1° to 2° F on a global basis is a dramatic change for agriculture. For instance, in the mid-1800s, annual average temperatures in the midwestern states were nearly 3°F lower than those of the 1952 to 1962 period. If the next one hundred years behave as the past, annual temperature fluctuations may decrease by as much as 3°F. Changes from year to year within a given decade may range a half a degree.

Dramatically spotlighting the issue are the severe droughts and consequent famines of western Africa. That drought was preceded by favorable weather periods which probably stimulated overdevelopment of the area. Scientists say that livestock losses coupled with the improved climate may have created a load that the marginal areas could not support during the drought. The increased populations exacerbated the subsequent food shortage. That drought ended with summer rains, although periods of deficient rainfall are often characteristic of a region's highly variable climate. Some climatologists feel that the recent drought years in the west African Sahel fell within normal expectations.

Recent studies of temperatures and precipitation in the United States found no dependable prediction potential. In fact, these studies illustrate that when a trend increases in one area, such as temperature increasing over time, it is usually also decreasing in another area. There evidently tends to be compensation on a hemispheric and global basis. These relationships also exist over oceanic areas. The possibility of simultaneous trends in the same direction in the food-producing regions of the world cannot be ruled out. This, of course, means a possibility of climatic change that could lead to either famine or feast.

Today, United Nations experts feel that world food reserves are no more than sufficient to compensate for one single year's bad harvest that might result from natural weather and climate fluctuations. Although the 20th century has witnessed unparalleled advances both in man's ability to produce abundant food harvests, the age-old threat of crop failure due to climate remains exactly the same.

Currently, the world has the technological capability to deal with many future agriculture contingencies arising from climate fluctuations. But the earth's need for food increases every year. For example, food for over 4 billion people was needed during 1977. It is projected that by the year 2000, food will be needed for 6 billion people. The developed nations have almost doubled their agricultural output during the past fifty years, while the output of undeveloped countries has increased by only 10 to 15 percent over those years.

Even though the total annual food supply has tended to increase in the past, it does not necessarily increase every year. In some cases, less food has been produced in some recent years than in the decades immediately preceding them. Depletion of grain reserves, malnutrition, starvation, and political unrest have generally occurred when food supplies do not meet the demands. Scientists therefore conclude that with the increasing demand of growing populations, food supplies may fail to balance with needs more frequently than they have in the past. Food production begins with a natural resource base: water and solar energy. And, these are directly affected by the climate.

## The Climatic Inputs

Both climate and weather determine and control the rates of photosynthesis and the resulting crop production. Climate changes over decades or a century are not as

significant to food production as fluctuations during a
season or a few years. A field of corn or wheat does not
escape undamaged from drought, floods, sun, hail, or excessive winds. Obviously, fluctuations in weather and
climate, from dry to wet, warm to cold, calm to windy,
always add uncertainty or risk to the production of food
and have greater disaster when they take place in regions
of "breadbasket."

But it's not just crops that are affected. Fluctuations
in climate and weather also affect livestock. Cold and
heat will reduce gains in weight and even kill livestock, or
reduce milk and egg production. The production of
livestock depends largely on forage and other crops for
feed. During favorable years, animal herds often increase, whereas continued drought (as California has experienced in 1976 and 1977) force farmers to reduce
livestock operations or damage pastures and ranges by
permitting overgrazing.

## Agriculturally Important Climatic Variables

First and foremost, agricultural production is determined
and influenced by the amount, intensity, and distribution
of rain. Although soil erosion is a natural on-going process which takes place regardless of land use, it is accelerated by excessive and intense rain. When rain falls
slowly, most soils can absorb it without erosion due to
runoff. In the tropics, rainfall is usually concentrated in
one or two annual periods. In many of the temperate
areas, such as the United States, monthly rain is not even-
ly distributed throughout the year. For instance, in the
semiarid areas of the northern Great Plains, precipitation
records reveal that while virtually all winter rains in
North and South Dakota occur in hourly amounts of less
than 2 inches, July thunderstorms will sometimes produce
more than 3 to 5 inches per hour. Thus, for water
resources management, areas of scant or excessive rain

generally are of major concern. Regions with excessive rain usually develop dense forests, which naturally protect the soil from erosion. Of course, the opposite would be true of those areas where there is little rain.

Wind may directly erode soil and can also force loss of soil moisture, loss of plant water, and evaporation losses from reservoirs. Wind erosion is a serious problem on dry, bare soils, and the most vulnerable geographic regions are those with low average annual rainfall. The problem is especially critical where there are steady prevailing winds over large, fairly level land masses.

Air temperature is yet another common climate determinant of agriculture and is probably the most widely used atmospheric indicator of both short- and long-term climate fluctuations. Temperatures affect the flux of water vapor and for this reason are significant to plant water status, soil drying, and irrigation practices.

Perhaps the most worrisome agriculturally important climatic variable to both the earth scientist and the farmer is drought. Climatic fluctuations leading to prolonged deficiencies in rainfall together with warmer temperatures are of particular concern to agricultural production as illustrated by the climatic events which led to the dust bowl conditions of the 1930s.

## The Great Drought of 1977

During the early months of 1977, the tragedy of the drought along the Pacific west coast was not given the spectacular publicity accorded the blizzard burying Buffalo. For those living west of the Rockies, it was an almost unending series of beautiful, spring-like days. However, few were enjoying the warm, calm weather. The increasing prospect of a disaster never before experienced had everyone worried. The ramifications were staggering.

For one, they raised again basic questions of how the west, and for that matter the nation, should use one of its

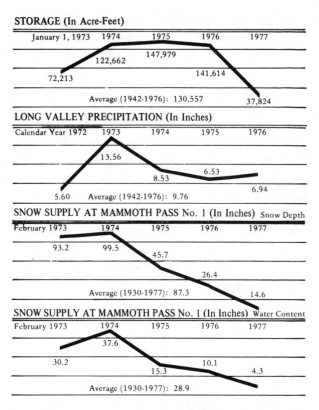

**STORAGE (In Acre-Feet)**

| January 1, 1973 | 1974 | 1975 | 1976 | 1977 |
|---|---|---|---|---|
| 72,213 | 122,662 | 147,979 | 141,614 | 37,824 |

Average (1942-1976): 130,557

**LONG VALLEY PRECIPITATION (In Inches)**

| Calendar Year 1972 | 1973 | 1974 | 1975 | 1976 |
|---|---|---|---|---|
| 5.60 | 13.56 | 8.53 | 6.53 | 6.94 |

Average (1942-1976): 9.76

**SNOW SUPPLY AT MAMMOTH PASS No. 1 (In Inches)** Snow Depth

| February 1973 | 1974 | 1975 | 1976 | 1977 |
|---|---|---|---|---|
| 93.2 | 99.5 | 45.7 | 26.4 | 14.6 |

Average (1930-1977): 87.3

**SNOW SUPPLY AT MAMMOTH PASS No. 1 (In Inches)** Water Content

| February 1973 | 1974 | 1975 | 1976 | 1977 |
|---|---|---|---|---|
| 30.2 | 37.6 | 15.3 | 10.1 | 4.3 |

Average (1930-1977): 28.9

A year-by-year comparative record of stored water and precipitation at Long Valley reservoir, the main storage facility for Los Angeles, plus the state of snow at Mammoth Pass No. 1, the major supplier of water to Long Valley.

most vital resources—its water—and just how much population growth the available water could sustain. As the west coast faced serious drought conditions, a world perennially short of food might not be able to look to America for easing its hunger. Domestic food prices began to increase, job layoffs followed as water and hydroelectric-hungry industries reduced their operations. Added to the effects of the east's frigid winter, the drought posed new dangers of inflation and unemployment, threatening President Carter's economic stimulus and budget-balancing goals.

But most of the anxiety of those living in the arid areas of the "Great Western Drought" was over what might happen, rather than what had already occurred. Many climatologists believe that the 1977 drought is threateningly similar to the conditions which preceded the drought and famine days of the mid-1930s.

For example, thousands of wells were drying up throughout the midwest. The U.S. Geological Survey estimated that 1,900 wells in Minnesota, another 1,400 in Michigan, and 500 more in Wisconsin were already dry. In California and the Pacific northwest, water users were digging deeper into the earth to locate whatever moisture there was. Parts of the Great Plains states were experiencing a drop in ground water levels, prompting drilling activity for irrigation water. But such pumping, once water was discovered, could cause agricultural lands to sink in certain regions.

In California, residents were little concerned about the worst which lay ahead. They were too preoccupied with the present, which had already brought enough trouble. While many northern California communities faced mandatory household rationing of water, other thirsty communities were practicing voluntary conservation. People were suddenly conscious of the wasteful ways in which they were using water: 40 gallons for a full bathtub, 20 gallons for a long shower, 35 gallons to wash dishes, 8 to 10 gallons to flush a toilet, 12 gallons a minute to sprinkle a lawn. All Californians were urged to cut consumption by 25 percent in their homes. One water-saving step that was recommended was for plastic bottles that reduce volume but not velocity of water ("toilet dams") to be installed in tanks. Meanwhile, Senator S. I. Hayakawa was offering his own advice on water saving techniques. "Urination," he said, "does not really require a flush," leading to the quip by some, "No pull for a pee." All over the state, and especially in the north, public restrooms were closed for lack of water, and others put up signs requesting you to flush only if it was absolutely necessary.

The water shortage was no laughing matter as some neighbors began battling each other. In Sacramento, state agencies reported hundreds of citizens writing or telephoning to complain of others who were secretly washing their cars or sprinkling their lawns at night. The two-year drought also caused the long-standing tensions between northern and southern California to flare up again. In and around Los Angeles, as well as throughout southern California, sprinklers were spewing water at the usual rate, swimming pools were emptied and refilled, and car washing was at full peak. Northern Californians were especially angry over plans of private real estate developers in Orange County to fill a man-made lake with more than a billion gallons of water from the north!

While the shortage of water was angrily pitting one against the other, and while some small communities that depended upon their own wells and reservoirs were nearly out of water, the most devastating consequence of the drought was on agriculture and food production. Some 87 percent of all California's water is used in agribusiness operations. While sprinklers were still dousing rows upon rows of lettuce and greens in the Salinas Valley, cherry trees farther to the north were drying up. In a state which supplies 28 percent of the nation's food, the northern irrigation systems pumping from ever-diminishing underground water tables were bringing up only air. Economists were speculating that even if rainfall returned to normal, at least $2 billion in crop losses were expected in California, to say nothing of Oregon, Washington, and Idaho.

In the Pacific northwest, the drought's full impact hit in the summer of 1977, when the lack of snowpack added to the water crisis. At the 6,500 foot level on Mount Hood, for example, the usual February snowpack is 145 inches.

Workers erect a mast with fire-weather-meteorological sensors at a Morgan Hill, California forestry installation for a satellite watch of forest fire danger.

By March of 1977, the snowlevel was only 22 inches. Of course, it is the snowpack which replenishes the reservoirs, streams, and irrigation ditches. With only a modest runoff Oregon and Washington officials estimated as much as a $2 billion economic loss. Not only this, but the Pacific northwest's forests were so dry and flammable that Oregon Governor Robert Straub hired 500 unemployed workers to train as fire fighters. He also recommended the creation of a four-state regional fire-fighting task force to coordinate the war against all the expected fires during the summer and fall.

As the levels of streams, rivers, and reservoirs fell, the Pacific northwest experienced huge hydroelectric power shortages. Unlike other sections of the nation, the northwest depends upon water power for over 90 percent of its electrical needs. It was necessary to make up the shortages by more expensive means of electrical generation—fossil-fuel burning plants and purchases from other suppliers.

But for California, the dry period presented a two-fold danger: a lack of moisture to nourish either the winter crops already planted (or the crops scheduled to be planted in the spring) and the lack of green grazing land which would force cattlemen either to sell off their thin animals at low prices or fatten them on expensive trucked-in feed. As the cost of feed soared, ranchers virtually dumped herds.

Perhaps more than any other food producer, the cattleman was hardest hit. The cattlemen who sold out during 1976 were the lucky ones. For example, Leo Fitzgerald, manager of the Stockton, California, Livestock Market, said, "In 1977, the cows and calves stand thin on skimpy range. Even though it's spring, the grass should be growing by leaps and bounds. And that is when cheap grains are put on cattle. But now the rancher has to feed them $96 a ton alfalfa or other feed. Cows don't make money. They cost money. Ranchers say a grown cow sold today has cost them $100. Keep it longer and it may cost you $150. A small herd of 200 has probably lost $20,000."

The auction yards from Stockton north to the Shasta Livestock Auction Yards at Cottonwood report more herds being "liquidated" every week at the sales. And, the prices are making grown cowmen cry.

In the spring of 1977, banks and other lenders were standing behind the cattlemen whenever they could. The Production Credit Association in Livermore, California, owned by its customers, had $18 million in agricultural loans out, about 65 percent on livestock. Said Tim Hay, the manager, "We've taken the approach that we're going to try to carry these people as long as we think they have an opportunity to recover. We weathered through last year and obviously most people weren't able to pay their loans. But we're still confident the weather will change."

But will it?

If another dry year like the previous two occurred, most of California's farmers and ranchers would be forced off the land. Rural communities, suffering from a shortage of farm dollars, would begin experiencing an economic ripple effect with unemployment leading to more unemployment. As food prices rise, quality, particularly in fruit, would decline. With everyone under mandatory water rationing, electrical power shortages would be a reality.

Ronald Robie, Director of the California Department of Water Resources, says, "The outlook is gloomy indeed if 1978 turns into a third dry year in a row. And even if there's a return to normal, it will still be pretty bleak. Besides the problem of emptied reservoirs and lowered ground water tables, dry watersheds will absorb much of the precipitation that occurs. Runoff will not be normal, even with normal amounts of precipitation. I don't know what next year will be like, but it's prudent to assume the worst." Meanwhile, agricultural economists were anticipating at least an 8 percent increase in food prices.

Thus, all weather and climatic events are crucial to plant and animal production—but rain is the primary factor. Excess water is a frequent problem in humid and subhumid areas. Although water deficits sometimes occur in these areas, deficiencies occur every year in arid and semiarid zones. Because of water's importance to agriculture, conservation of water, efficiencies in its use and questions of its ownership are critical issues in research and public policy.

### Strategies for Developing Nations

The farmer struggling in less developed nations is not only at the mercy of lack of capital, skills of management, and incentives, but also climatic fluctuations which influence water and land resources, plant breeding, crop, pest, and livestock management. In spite of contemporary man's

tremendous technological achievements in food cultiva-
tion and preparation, more people starved during the first
seven years of the 1970s than in the previous two centuries put together. During the 1974 World Food Con-
ference in Rome, as well as subsequent conferences, an
international food reserve has been proposed. But,
studies have been emphasizing that current annual
harvests are not adequate to establish an international
reserve of any magnitude. Despite the recent expanded
wheat crops of the United States, Canada, and Australia,
and the abundant rice harvests in Southeast Asia, world
stocks of major food grains are critically low. The experience of the past 15 years questions the ability of an
international distribution system to respond in time to major food crises during famines.

The widening gap in most developing countries between demand and production, coupled with rising prices
of imported food and petroleum makes accelerated
development of food production a priority. A first step for
every nation (especially for those chronically short of
foodstuffs) would be to organize for short-term climate
fluctuations. No methods have as yet been conceived of
forestalling, or even mitigating, the effects of major
climatic shifts and catastrophes.

To illustrate how complex the world pattern of
climates is, a short review of how weather changes is in
order.

As a consequence of the way the planet revolves
around the sun and rotates upon its axis, the low latitudes
or tropics receive more solar energy than do the middle
and higher latitudes. On the average, however, the low
latitudes receive more energy than they lose, while the
reverse is the case in middle and higher latitudes. To correct this energy imbalance there develops a large-scale
transfer of heat toward the poles, accomplished through
atmospheric and oceanic circulations. Earth rotation
takes place from west to east and the frictional effects of

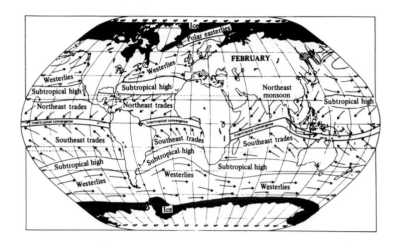

the earth's surface upon air flow causes these circulations to be relatively complex. But since solar energy and atmospheric and oceanic circulations are distributed in an organized fashion over the earth, these, operating jointly, produce recognizable world patterns of temperature and rain, the two most important climatic elements.

If the globe's surface were homogeneous with either land or water and was lacking in terrain irregularities, atmospheric pressure, winds, temperature, and rain would be arranged in zonal or east-west belts. Such a zonal arrangement prevails in the more uniform southern hemisphere. But the fact that the earth's surface is not uniform and is instead composed of continents and oceans whose heating and frictional effects upon winds are quite in contrast, there results a breakdown of the zonal belts of pressure and winds into cells, a fact which greatly complicates temperature and rainfall distributions.

In spite of all these complications imposed by a non-homogeneous earth surface, and even though the great land masses have a variety of shapes, dimensions, and

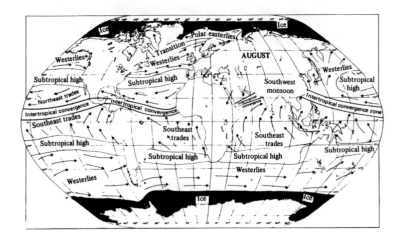

terrain features, there is nonetheless a clear and recognizable world pattern in each of the climatic elements.
Each element is sufficiently regular and dependable so
that it produces relatively similar climatic conditions in
similar latitudinal and continental locations on most of
the great land masses, even though they are separated by
great distances. It is this repetition of climatic conditions
which make it possible to classify the numerous regional
and local climates into a few types.

Given such repetition of climatic conditions, realistic
strategies reducing the farmer's vulnerability to weather
fluctuations can be developed. The governments of developing nations are generally focusing on those food production responses which are directly related to fluctuations in weather and climate. These include increased
water supplies by publicly financed irrigation schemes,
establishing water catchments, digging more wells, desalting seawater and brackish water, soil and water conservation, improved farm management practices and developing and introducing new drought-tolerant food
varieties.

| CHARACTERISTIC WEATHER CHANGES ASSOCIATED WITH THE PASSAGE OF COLD AND WARM FRONTS | | | | |
|---|---|---|---|---|
| WEATHER ELEMENTS | COLD FRONT | | WARM FRONT | |
| | BEFORE | AFTER | BEFORE | AFTER |
| Wind direction | Southwest | Northwest | South | Southwest |
| Wind speed | Moderate | High | Low—moderate | Moderate |
| Temperature | Warm | Cold | Cool | Warm |
| Clouds | Cumulus | Clear | Stratus | Cirrocumulus |
| Precipitation | Yes—heavy | No | Yes—moderate | Yes—showery |
| Humidity | High | Low | Moderate | High |
| Pressure | Low | High | High | Low |

| TYPICAL FEATURES OF AIR MASSES THAT AFFECT WEATHER IN THE UNITED STATES | | | |
|---|---|---|---|
| AIR MASS TYPE | SEASON | TEMPERATURE | HUMIDITY |
| Arctic | Winter | Very cold | Very dry |
| Continental Polar | Winter | Cold | Dry |
| | Summer | Cool | Variable |
| Maritime Polar | Winter | Mild | Moist |
| | Summer | Cool | Moist |
| Continental Tropical | Summer | Hot | Dry |
| Maritime Tropical | Winter | Warm | Moist |
| | Summer | Very warm | Moist |
| Equatorial | Summer | Very warm | Moist |

Of these food production responses, the creation of new drought-tolerant crops is the most promising. In arid and semiarid zones, modern irrigation methods have permitted man to overcome climatic and weather constraints on the development of modern agriculture. The improved varieties of grain which led to the Green Revolution were especially adapted for use with irrigation. Now, say food experts, there is a great need to develop other improved food varieties, not only of grains but also crops that are less dependent upon irrigation. In most less-developed nations available water supplies are barely adequate.

Developing new supplies is going to be expensive, while improving the efficiency of use of existing irrigation works faces difficult institutional obstacles.

Scientists feel that the development and dispersion of new crop varieties with increased drought tolerance would actually improve the income and diet of the farmers and people of less-developed nations. The yield advantage of improved over traditional varieties grown under dry-land conditions would perhaps be less than for varieties grown under irrigation, but the total increase in production would probably be as great, and the gains much more widely distributed because there are many more dry-land farmers than irrigation farmers. Yet, population and food experts feel that with time, a critical factor, the costs of development and introduction of new varieties are considered moderate. Benefits, say the authorities, are also ranked "moderate."

*Marine Food Production and the Changing Climate*

Perhaps our greatest food potential rests in the nearby oceans. But even in ocean environments changes have occurred, resulting in major declines in production in a number of fisheries. For instance, the Icelandic herring fishery during the early 1970s suffered a catch decline due to ocean climate change and overfishing. The catch fell from 750,000 tons per year in the late 1960s to about 50,000 tons in 1972 with nearly catastrophic consequences for Iceland's economy. The decline was initially caused by a change in the migration routes of the herring which was probably due to a change in the Icelandic ocean environment. During the late 1960s, increased ice cover developed compared to earlier years. The decline may also have been due to a shift in the atmospheric pressure system, which suggests stronger flow out of the northwest in the 1960s than in the previous decade. This would tend to drive the ice pack south. On top of all this, the ocean currents in the general area of Iceland appear to have shifted dramatically during this time. These events would certainly be expected to affect migration routes of the herring, perhaps keeping the fish out of the Icelandic fleet's range.

The very low Alaska salmon harvests in 1973 and 1974 have been blamed on a climatic shift in the Bering Sea during the early 1970s, resulting because of the unusually severe 1971-1972 cold years. Land stations in Alaska during the winter of 1970-1971 reported all-time low temperature readings. The sea surface temperatures in the Aleutian Islands region in 1971 and 1972 were the lowest in twenty years. The beginning of these sea and air temperature declines appeared to coincide with an unusual southward penetration of an Arctic ice pack.

Climatologists were uncertain whether this was merely a chance relationship or a cause-and-effect relationship between ice and sea temperatures, or whether both events were related to some other still undetermined climatic variable. Some scientists correlate cold sea temperatures to the increasing northerly winds and large changes in the north Pacific atmospheric circulation, possibly resulting in an extension of the ice pack. Severe environmental stresses induced by this drop in temperature could affect salmon survival in all phases of its life in lakes, streams, and the ocean.

In biological development, the stage of egg and larval existence is critical. Recent analysis of variations in the number of yearly menhadens in the Atlantic and mackerel in the Pacific suggest that annual variations in surface water temperature during this critical stage of egg and larva may be the dominant cause of variations from season to season in size of exploitable populations. Although scientists say that some of this variation might be attributed to fluctuation in the size of the spawning stock, it's been proven that a positive relationship exists between the numbers of fish caught and surface water

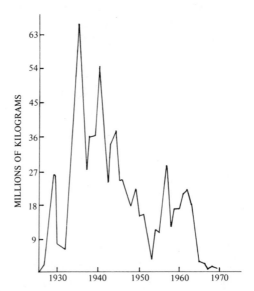

California Pacific mackerel landings 1926-1970.

temperature, which of course is influenced by atmospheric circulation. Several years of variations in surface
temperature in the mackerel spawning grounds off Baja
California, coupled with continued heavy fishing pressure
caused a sharp decline in catch and the ultimate collapse
of the fishery.

El Niño (a change in current patterns and sea surface temperatures off the west coast of South America) is
a dramatic example of a short-term climate shift with a
disastrous effect on fish catches. Climatologists say the
last major El Niño appearance in 1973, together with excessive over-fishing, dramatically reduced the catches of
anchovies from 13 million tons in 1971 (about a fourth of
the total world catch of all fish) to about 2 million tons in
1974.

The processes by which El Niño affects the anchovy
population are not yet understood. The phenomenon is
usually characterized by high sea temperatures and rain-

fall in the coastal areas of Ecuador and northern Peru. The temperature of the ocean surface near the equator in the eastern Pacific is higher in *El Niño* years: 6° F warmer in November, 1972, than in November, 1973. These differences, say the climatologists, are probably related to changes in atmospheric circulation over wide areas of the earth, especially over the United States and the north Pacific.

Coastal temperatures along Peru show that fairly strong *El Niños* developed in 1925, 1941, 1957, and 1972, and weaker ones in 1930, 1943, 1953, 1965, and 1969. One climatologist predicted a weak *El Niño* in early 1975 based upon studies of variations in atmospheric pressure differences between Australia and Easter Island. These were part of variations in the overall atmospheric circulation called the Southern Oscillation. Apparently, sea temperatures rose dramatically to the east of the Galapagos in early 1975. However, these warm temperatures did not reach the Peruvian coast and apparently did not affect the anchovy population.

Thus, years of good fishing appear to be related to warm winters the preceding year along the eastern seaboard and poor years to cold winters. Some scientists have actually identified the two different kinds of atmospheric circulation that predominate. Poor catches are usually associated with strong air circulation in the eastern United States, which tends to carry colder continental air masses over the southeastern seaboard. High ridges tend to block storms of northern origin so that air masses of more tropical features take over, leading to warmer water temperatures. In addition to influencing abundance and distribution of fish stocks, climatic changes occurring on the fishing grounds can influence catches by helping or hindering the fishing operation.

Food experts across the world are asking for improved knowledge of climatic change in the oceans and the effect of change on living marine resources. It is extremely important for food experts to be able to predict the environmental changes and size of annual catches, since a large year's catch may lead to a large increase in fishing effort in subsequent years. If this happens, overinvesting and overfishing in subsequent years will result in reduced quantities. A large year's catch followed by several poor years is potentially disastrous to the fishing industry as well as to the stocks of fish. Knowledge of the effects of climate change on fish replenishment and the ability to predict year by year strength is necessary if the world's fisheries are to operate at maximum sustaining yields.

## Climate Change and Health

Questions dealing with how weather and climate affect human beings are being answered by the science of biometeorology. Researchers in this relatively little-worked new field are attempting to correlate the interaction between two of the most complex systems on earth: the atmosphere and the mysterious functioning of living organisms. Do people really "feel" climate change? Are Mrs. McCall's aching, arthritic joints really quicker than the National Weather Service's computer forecasts? Is it practical to move from one state to another because "the climate is better?"

The belief that human health and disease are allied with daily and seasonal weather probably is as old as the human race. One of the first to write about it was the Greek physician Hippocrates. In his book *On Airs, Waters, and Places,* he describes different reactions of his patients to hot and cold wind. Hippocrates also theorized that epidemics were related to seasonal weather changes.

But Hippocrates wasn't the first to watch the sky for implications of sickness. Priests and physicians of many early Chaldean, Egyptian, Babylonian, and Assyrian cultures believed that life (as opposed to death) was associated with breathing air, even though air itself was a mystery. Some diseases arrived with one season while others arrived with another. Cold, rainy spells were followed by a certain type of sickness. Thus, clusters of stars and the zodiac were related to parts of the body and used to "treat" disease. One Egyptian text said, "If the constellation of Cancer becomes obscured, a fatal demon will possess the land and many deaths will occur."

Hippocrates wrote, "South wind induces dullness of hearing, dimness of vision, heaviness of head; but if the north wind prevails, cough, afflictions of the throat occur." Writers during the next several hundred years conceived their own ideas. Celsus, for example, recommended sea voyages and new climates for a variety of ills. Galen, on the other hand, advised mountain climates. He also insisted he found a difference in the strength and resistance of babies born during certain moon phases.

Weather-oriented medical philosophers were also common in ancient China. Huang Ti said in 2650 B.C. that heat hinders the heart and cold impairs the lungs. He also felt that the west wind was bad for the heart, ribs, and breast, while the north wind was bad for the hips and kidneys. During A.D. 600, India's Susruta popularized health resorts by recommending that the king vacation in a dry locality during the "dangerous rainy season."

As the centuries passed, astrology became meshed with medicine. During the Renaissance, French and Italian physicians listed almost five hundred weather signs which influenced health. In the 17th and 18th centuries, several books were published describing weather and magnetic fields, barometric pressure and lunar tides. Glisson wrote in 1650 that infantile rickets were caused by the foggy climate and that sunlight might be important in prevention.

In the 18th century, it was believed that climatic factors were responsible for fevers and epidemics. With the arrival of the 19th century, scientists hit upon micro-organisms and less emphasis was placed upon climatic factors.

Careful scientific investigations have been conducted only over the past few decades. These careful studies have begun to show intricate interactions between climatic change and health. One of the difficulties of such investigations is that no two human beings are exactly alike. People have different genes, statures, states of nutrition. And, most important, different people change at different ages.

No human being is totally immune to the atmospheric environment. We are physically adapted to a narrow range of temperature. Our metabolic mechanisms are suited for air temperature around 77° F. There is a limited range above and below this temperature where survival is possible. At lower temperatures, greater muscular activity will raise body heat. At higher temperatures sweating restores thermal equilibrium. Evaporation of sweat uses up extra heat energy taken from the body. This process works well when humidities are low, but at high humidities, the evaporative cooling will not work. Overheating occurs and heat stroke can result. Infants whose heat regulatory mechanism is not yet fully developed and senior citizens with impaired circulatory systems are most likely to suffer.

Wind is an important factor when the weather gets cold. It blows away the thin protective air layer near the skin. We attempt to keep this insulation intact by wearing thicker and thicker clothing as the temperature drops. Various combinations of air temperature and wind speed have been combined into a wind chill index, which tells you how cold it is in combination with the wind. Temperature readings alone express only the temperature of calm air.

Between the dangerous limits of heat and wind chill, there are comfort and discomfort sensations. These, of course, are widely differentiated, often governed by a person's nutritional state. Obese people suffer more from heat, while undernourished people are very sensitive to cold.

Because skin separates the body from the external world, it senses and transmits to the body and the brain many of the changes taking place in the atmosphere. The system works well as long as the skin is healthy, but when it is scarred, it flashes pain signals. Temperature and moisture changes and possible electrical conditions in the atmosphere induce a tension between the scar tissue and healthy skin. Deformed skin, such as corns, act the same way.

Throughout history, soldiers suffering from grievous wounds and amputations have forecast weather changes. Falling barometric pressure, followed by rain, the typical symptoms of a warm weather front, caused pain. But pain reactions also occurred with cold fronts, and rain showers, as well as to atmospheric electric phenomena.

Very similar weather conditions affect arthritics. Termed biotropic, these conditions are clearly linked to humidity changes. Scientists say that according to all their observations rising humidities by themselves are not enough, the barometric pressure has to fall, too.

The best known case of a disease allegedly related to weather is the common cold. Is it really a weather-caused illness? Medical experts say there is no easy answer. They know that it is a virus-caused disease, with the virus spreading from person to person. That virus cannot survive in extreme cold (human beings never have colds in the polar regions). In the moderate latitudes, the occurrence of colds reaches a pronounced peak during winter, primarily when people are confined indoors, schools are in session and the virus spreads epidemically.

Climatologists say they know very little about virus transport by atmospheric currents and their survival times in relation to weather. In this respect, they are much better informed about airborne allergies, the best known cause of which are various plant pollens carried by turbulent winds. On the warm days of spring and summer, the atmosphere is thermally unstable.

More harmful even than pollen are spores of fungi. They can float greater distances, sometimes 1500 miles. Heavy wind storms may stir some of these fungi out of the ground and carry them along. One such fungus, which lives in both tame and wild bird excrement, causes lung diseases.

But the same atmosphere which musters up these organic irritants also helps to eliminate them. Rains cleanse the atmosphere of these, as well as man-made pollutants. The more frequently it rains, the cleaner the air.

So, welcomed in many respects, the changing weather plays a significant role in affecting physiological and pathological conditions. Rapid changes seem to initiate responses in the human body. H. E. Landberg, former Director of the Environmental Data Service and professor of meteorology of the University of Maryland, explains how six phases represent fairly well the complex totality of weather and how they can influence health.

Starting with cool, high pressure, with a few clouds and moderate winds, (1) followed by perfectly clear, dry, high pressure and little wind; (2) we get into considerable warming, steady or slightly falling pressure with some high clouds; (3) then warm, moist air gets into the lower layers, pressure falls, clouds thicken, winds pick up, and rain falls; (4) then an abrupt change takes place, lighter rain falls and is accompanied by cold, gusty winds and rapidly rising pressure and falling humidity; (5) finally with further rising pressure and diminishing clouds, temperatures reach low levels and humidities also drop.

Such phases are not long, generally ranging from a few days to a few weeks, but weather phases have been correlated with the joys and tragedies of human life. In order to do this, biometeorologists rely on hospital records.

For instance, calm, warm weather stimulates the body very little. It generally makes few demands on us and most of these are met with proper clothing and housing. In contrast, precipitous drops in pressure, humidity, or temperature are turbulent and violent. In some unexplained way, they agitate and stir people up—ask any classroom teacher!

Death seems to follow these same phases. Heart attacks also show a peak during phases 3 and 4, but show a decline in phases 1 and 5. Bleeding ulcers, migraines, and spasmodic diseases generally appear during phase 4.

Not only does weather affect health, disease, birth and death, it is also often responsible for our moods and behavior. Weather phase 3 shows a clear jump in the occurrence of suicide over the phases. When it comes to learning, children do not learn well when it is hot and sticky. Riots generally occur when atmospheric conditions are uncomfortable.

Examples of indirect effects of weather on human health include the mosquito's danger. The mosquito can only survive where temperatures are sufficiently high and standing water permit them to go through their life cycle. There is a distinct malaria climate where the mosquito species carrying and transmitting the disease can survive. Unfortunately this climate prevails over large areas of the tropics, so that the disease still remains the world's greatest public health menace. Other disease-carrying parasites have their own environmental needs and if their temperatures, humidity, and water needs are met, they multiply rapidly.

Another dramatic example is the bubonic plague. The flea that carries the disease to man begins its life cycle on a rat. After prolonged dry spells, more plague carriers exist. In contrast, after heavy rains, the number of carriers drop, because rats drown.

Today, climatologists are wondering about the relation of weather to the effects of drugs. America is in an age of pill-popping and some evidence already exists that the same dosage will have greater or lesser effects on different days. Because many patients administer drugs to themselves, it's imperative that knowledge be gained on weather-steered drug responses. More sensitivity to health-related information by those who issue forecasts would be very beneficial. If this is someday possible, weather-sensitive people could learn how to better cope with the atmospheric steering of their symptoms.

# IV

# Predicting, Controlling, and Modifying Climates

*The greater man's "mastery" of nature, the more essential is his understanding of causes in order that mastery be disciplined to obedience.*

Harvey Brooks

The dream of every climatologist is to achieve the ability to predict changes in the atmosphere. But despite all the modern instruments and meteorological methods, weather forecasting of any kind remains at best an inexact science. Dreams of actually doing something about the weather are unrealistic. Was the "Big Freeze and Drought of 1977" really necessary? Scientists say yes. Despite some limited successes in making rain on demand, most believe that as far as the foreseeable future is concerned, prediction, control, and modification of climate is unlikely.

What is more probable is that the weather will continue to play with its would-be forecasters, embarrassing them with rain when they call for clear skies, drought when they predict rain. Contemporary weathermen are basing their forecasts on ever-evolving knowledge about how the world's weather machine works. Today, satellites track storms from high above the earth. Monitoring stations provide agencies such as the National Weather Service with thousands of readings daily, recording air and sea-surface temperatures, barometric pressures, relative humidity, and wind speeds and directions. Highly complicated and sophisticated computers enable weathermen to make calculations in minutes which might otherwise require months.

With all these aids, short-term forecasting is quite reliable. For example, a meteorologist observes that a mass of cold, dry air is moving down from western Canada at 600 miles a day. The scientist can check its direction, figure out how long it will take for its front to collide with a warm, moist air mass sitting over New York and predict where and when the resulting rains will begin. Thus, weathermen can predict two or three days ahead with relative accuracy.

However, beyond these two or three days, the batting average of the meteorologist begins to diminish. Five-day forecasts are considerably less accurate. A thirty-day forecast is little better than a layman's hunch. Says Warren Washington of the National Center for Atmospheric Research in Boulder, Colorado, "It's really like playing dice. The odds are that a thirty-day forecast will be better than a purely random guess, but not much better."

In spite of this, Jerome Namias of California's Scripps Institute of Oceanography and Donald Gilman, Director of the National Weather Service's Long-Range Prediction Group, used advanced theories and masses of data in the fall of 1976 to accurately forecast the general pattern (if not the intensity) of 1977s weird winter weather patterns. In contrast, the U.S. Weather Service's thirty-day forecast for the period ending January 15 was only partially correct. The service accurately forecasted below-normal temperatures for New England and upstate

New York, but incorrectly foresaw near average temperatures for the rest of New York and most of the south and
midwest. Below normal rain for most of the northern half
of the nation was predicted, but not the snows which crip-
pled Buffalo.

Climatologists agree that there are still huge gaps in
the meteorological data that they need for more precise
predictions. There are huge areas of the southern hemisphere, for example, for which no surface temperature,
wind velocity, or barometric pressure readings exist.
More work must be done on developing computer models
of the weather.

But no matter how advanced the tools and theories,
most meteorologists admit that certain aspects of climatic
behavior cannot be predicted because of major problems
involved. First of all, climatologists are confronted with
time and space as well as high-frequency turbulent fluctuations to climate changes occurring over thousands of
years. To scientists, therefore, phenomena of all kinds are
significant. Turbulent fluctuations are responsible for the
transfer and dispersion of pollutants, storms provide
cities with water, while climate changes create dust
bowls or raise lake levels.

Operational weather-prediction capabilities just a
few years ago were, for the most part, limited to the time
interval of twelve hours to two days. During the past five
years, operational forecasting centers and research in-
stitutes have developed more sophisticated models which
have resulted in major improvements in forecast accuracy. The National Meteorological Center now issues
regular 72-hour prognostic charts and is usually successful in predicting new storm development. But, the
lack of global data is the primary reason the period of
useful forecasts is restricted to a few days. The newly
proposed World Weather Program is intended to extend
the prediction limit to something approaching the
"theoretical limit" of about two weeks. Better forecasts

of cyclones, planetary waves, hurricanes, and urban smog should result. Already, progress has been made in acquiring global data and in developing numerical models, so that predictive capability now has been somewhat extended beyond two or three days.

On shorter periods, numerical prediction models have been applied to a minor extent to phenomena such as fronts. Progress has been limited due to the computational requirements and to the fact that vertical convection and condensation play such important parts in short-period phenomena. Although numerical models have successfully simulated the dynamics of convection, the statistics have not been incorporated in the models of the large-scale circulation. This, say meteorologists, has been the most serious limitation on progress in weather prediction.

Despite the fact that little predictive capability can be claimed for time scales less than twelve hours, a significant amount of climate change does occur on these smaller time and space scales. Tornadoes, thunderstorms, and other destructive storms are included here. However, predictions are nonexistent in terms of intensity, location, and occurring time. Terminal forecasts are made for aircraft, and probability forecasts are issued for severe storms expected to occur in large regions. Short-period severe storm warnings are issued in certain areas.

Short-range prediction has not advanced as rapidly as have predictions on the larger scales for two reasons: First, according to meteorologists, there are severe mathematical and theoretical difficulties in creating general prediction models for these smaller scales. The time scales are so short that the relation between wind velocity and pressure is not valid. A second major difficulty deals with the time required for observations needed to describe the phenomena. The data necessary to describe these small-scale features are numerous and the time

Monitoring climatic change equipment inside an
atmospheric research plane.

available for processing, interpreting, and disseminating
the results is very short.

Can one realistically hope to improve short-range
prediction in the face of these difficulties? Experts conclude that there are several avenues which could lead to
major improvements. For periods extending from a few
minutes to perhaps 2 hours, some short-term features can
be successfully predicted by the simple extrapolation of
current conditions and rates of change. The crucial need
is to systematically apply modern technology to describe
the local weather as it develops and to communicate the
information. For instance, by means of existing technology the motion of a squall line or the occurrence of a thunderstorm could be shown on any local television screen,
so that the viewer would know just what to expect at his
doorstep or along his way to work within the next hour or
so. Utility companies might be able to anticipate abrupt

changes in customer demand provided they have reliable
information on significant short-period weather changes.
Now, critical minutes, and even hours often elapse between the time of observation and dissemination of the information. High-resolution satellite pictures often cannot be transmitted from data centers until hours have
elapsed.

Scientists say that although they have a fairly complete theoretical understanding of phenomena on the 12-
hour to 2-week periods, the corresponding predictive
capability for variations of the seasonal and longer
periods are virtually lacking. They do not know, for instance, the degree to which long-term variations may be
inherent in an atmosphere with fixed boundary conditions and composition. Many theories exist which relate
variations of the seasonal-to-annual scale to interaction
of the atmosphere with the upper layer of the ocean or
with the polar sea ice.

Scientists are not lacking in plausible hypotheses
which may explain weather fluctuations. The list of
"Grand Theories of Climate" grows. The oceans warm,
and evaporation increases, snows mount, ice caps build
and flow, and the planet cools, volcanoes trigger ice ages,
or ice sets off volcanoes. Inner churnings drive continents
which in turn sink and build mountains. The higher the
mountains, the more they block and change circulation of
the atmosphere and the seas. The sun may blink in total
energy output. Sunspots may reveal such variations and
be the key to short-term climate changes.

But despite all these theories, scientists still do not
know which are the most important in accounting for
climate change.

## Problems of Predicting Crop Production

There are many problems related to climate prediction.
As has been described, information on weather and

climate is crucial to agricultural planning on both the global and local levels. The farmer can, to some extent, control production, but he is ultimately powerless against disastrous events or consistently unfavorable weather. The farmer's prices are increasingly determined by global, not local, conditions. The "breadbaskets" of the world have developed where a stable climate matches the soil and nutrient requirements of the crop. Crops grown on the outer edges of these breadbaskets are more susceptible to the variability of weather and climate.

Crop yield potentials can be predicted from models of various combinations of climatic variables. The combinations used depend upon the crop and the geographical area. In order to provide information necessary for crop production on a long-term as well as a short-term basis, the periods selected for analysis should be short and the areas small to make prediction of crop production feasible and to minimize the effect of averaging. In some drier regions, wheat yields have been estimated using figures for rain accumulated over an extended period of months, but averages for shorter time periods are generally used. Other systems use weekly and daily values of weather parameters. To be timely and useful for agriculture, climatic fluctuations for assessing yields must be considered for seasonal periods.

The best available seasonable forecasts for general use are the monthly and seasonal outlooks prepared by the National Weather Service of the National Oceanic and Atmospheric Administration. The temperature predictions of these forecasts have a probability of being correct 60 percent of the time, compared to the 50 percent probability of being correct from mere chance.

Since so many economic benefits could come from such successful prediction, why has no little progress been made achieving it?

Climatologists say that during the past twenty-five years, numerical models have been designed which simulate realistically the average large-scale structure of the global atmosphere. Some scientists feel that studies based upon models and their underlying theory tell us that there exists an inherent limit of a week or two in the predictability of detailed behavior of the atmosphere. They say that unless it can be demonstrated that current models are less predictable than the real atmosphere, it would seem that the possibility of detailed monthly or seasonal forecasts giving day-to-day information is impossible and that we must consider instead the possibility of forecasting the monthly or seasonal statistics of weather variables.

As has been mentioned, studies have indeed proven that most of the monthly and seasonal fluctuation averages are attributed to the effects of day-to-day fluctuations which by their very nature are unpredictable for periods beyond a week or two. These day-to-day fluctuations tend to hide the climatic change due to slowly acting influences, such as ocean surface temperature, soil moisture, snow and ice cover. Comparisons of the year-to-year variability of seasonal averages with the natural unpredictable changes to be expected, demonstrate that predictive ability is relatively small in midlatitudes and large in the tropics.

There are two approaches to the prediction of future climate:

(1) Statistical analysis of long-term climate information which offers relevant assessments of the impacts on agricultural production;

(2) Development and application of models of the climate systems developed by theory.

Climatologists plead for both approaches to be pursued, since it is essential that a worldwide weather bank be developed. The problem of just what climatic information the farming community and supporting agencies need, in what form it is needed, and just how to prepare and distribute the information in time for it to be useful are of particular importance. Conclusions concerning the impact of climate on agriculture depend upon the period of record selected for analysis. Projections based on data from a sample that was unusual in some areas can result in biased estimates.

Weather and climate data should be made available to the farmer in every community in a concise and easily comprehensible form. Since crops interact with weather and climate, the information presented must throw light on this interaction in its choice of data and time periods.

An understanding of the behavior of the climatic system is considered a necessary but not a sufficient prerequisite to a long-term climatic prediction capability, and that understanding is not yet at hand. When it is achieved, it may well be discovered that the behavior of the system is not inherently predictable, either because some climate-governing external influences are themselves unpredictable or because the system itself evolves in an undetermined manner. At present, not enough is known about the problem of climate predictability to determine whether long-term predictions are realistic. Climatologists say there is little prospect for this happening soon.

### Modifying Weather and Climate: A Dream or Realistic Goal?

Twenty-five years ago, scientists at the General Electric Company demonstrated through a series of field experiments that they could deliberately alter cloud formations and bring about rain. Since that time, weather modification has received a great deal of attention by climatologists and the general public. Laboratory and field investigations have expanded immensely the physics of clouds and rain. Indeed, the business of operational cloud seeding has mushroomed and extensive projects have been carried out in many nations for increasing and redistributing rainfall, suppressing lightning and hail, and for dissipating fog. But within all this, there has been controversy. Earth and atmospheric scientists have debated the interpretations of experiments and operational projects. Some operators have made contradictory and sometimes extravagant claims, while lawsuits have been filed to recover damages or to prevent cloud-seeding efforts. Federal and state government policy has been uncoordinated and contradictory, leaving the public confused. Indeed, in the past few years, the accidental change of weather and climate through various forms of human activities has brought about a growing concern.

The technical reasons for the long-continued controversy over cloud seeding (despite some significant advances) are that:

(1) scientists do not have a complete and accurate understanding of how clouds create raindrops and snowflakes;

(2) field observations usually have been inadequate in describing accurately the specific changes resulting from cloud-seeding efforts; and

(3) the effects of individual seeding experiments, even when successful, usually fall well within the natural variability of clouds and cloud systems.

In reviewing the history of weather modification, early man attempted to influence the weather by using a variety of tricks, including sacrificing virgins and staging rain dances. Renaissance Europeans, noticing that heavy rains seemed to follow battles, believed the precipitation was shaken loose from the clouds by cannon noise.

It was really Vincent Shaefer, a researcher for General Electric, who brought about the first man-determined rain. In 1946, he placed frozen carbon dioxide (dry ice) into a freezer and watched as a miniature cloud formed and snowflakes began falling. Several months later, collaborating with Irving Langmuir, he attempted his initial experiment on a massive scale. From an airplane, he dropped dry ice into a cloud. The ice pellets triggered the formation of ice crystals, which melted into rain as they descended through the various warm layers of the atmosphere. Today, cloud seeding with dry ice or with silver iodide (which provides the nuclei for the formation of ice crystals) is often carried out by the government and private rainmakers. The process has been used with some success to encourage rains over drought-parched western and midwest farmland. Cloud seeding has also been employed experimentally to weaken hurricanes. For example, during the fall of 1969, scientists seeded the clouds in the wall of the eye, or inner ring, of Hurricane Debbie. The wall expanded upward and outward, and its wind speeds decreased. In a second major attempt to influence the weather, the U.S. Department of Defense allocated $22 million to a seven-year program of cloud seeding to trigger rain over areas of southeast Asia during the Viet Nam conflict. The goal was to turn the Ho Chi Minh Trail into impassable muds. Military experts reported that the success was questionable, although they claimed they were able to induce as much as eight inches of rain to fall in a few days during May of 1971.

Even more elaborate weather-modification ideas have been suggested. For instance, Krafft Ehricke, a German-born rocket scientist, revived an earlier suggestion that huge orbiting mirrors be used to reflect sunlight onto the dark side of the earth, preventing crop freezes and perhaps raising average temperatures enough to forestall the new ice age that some German climatologists believe lies ahead. Other visionary schemes include the suggestion of paving large areas of desert with blacktop, which would absorb the sun's heat and warm the air above them, causing strong updrafts which would draw moist air in from nearby oceans.

Most climatologists are urging the acceleration of weather-modification research. The U.S. Bureau of Reclamation, Colorado State University, and other institu-

Tomorrow's weatherman will use an all-electronic
system for preparing daily forecasts and issuing
storm warnings. Computerized data-handling
with TV-type displays will greatly speed the job.

tions have conducted studies suggesting that carefully
designed cloud-seeding programs can indeed increase
snowfall in areas of the Rockies by 20 percent. Because of
this, Colorado officials appropriated nearly $175,000 for
seeding clouds in fourteen sections of the state. Dr. Lew
Grant of Colorado State's meteorology department feels
that cloud cover over the Rockies should be seeded
routinely during years of abnormally low snowfall. "As
far as I'm concerned," says Grant, "the medicine has
been on the shelf ready to use for five years."

Indeed, the past five years show that weather
modification has pushed forward on many problems—a
period of slow clarification of concepts and ideas rather
than of dramatic new discoveries. The most important
achievements have been in the analysis of convective
clouds and in the modifying of rain, the dynamics of convective clouds, the dynamics of hurricanes, fog dissipation, and hail suppression.

In terms of modifying rain, there is increasing but still somewhat ambiguous statistical evidence that rain from some types of cloud and storm systems can be modestly increased or redistributed by seeding techniques. Randomized experiments have indicated that silver iodide seeding may in some situations lead to increases in rain amounting to 10 to 30 percent. In other situations it has led to corresponding decreases in rain. In other cases, cloud seeding had little or no effect. The characteristics which determine rainfall increases from decreases in seeding rain clouds appear to be connected with the temperature and wind distributions. However, the exact role of these distinguishing characteristics in influencing the effects of seeding has not been adequately explained.

In other advances, the use of ground-based radar has brought about certain advances in analyzing the motion, liquid water, and ice in convective clouds. The creation of more advanced techniques has made possible still more accurate analysis of the three-dimensional distribution of the wind field, while satellite pictures have revealed organizations of convective clouds on a number of scales. Numerical models of convective clouds have been developed which can predict effects of heat release from ice-crystal growth initiated by seeding. Numerical experiments can be used to develop seeding operations which modify the location and intensity of the updraft and the height of the cloud top. A limited number of field tests of such models have already taken place and have yielded positive results suggesting that the vertical extent of some convective clouds can be increased by means of silver iodide seeding.

Another achievement in weather modification deals with the dynamics of hurricanes. Simple, numerical models of hurricanes have been used to simulate the development of hurricanes by specific modes of cloud seeding. For example, a field test of Hurricane Debbie in August of 1969 indicated a diminishing of wind speeds by

Above the eye of a hurricane in a NOAA monitoring aircraft.

30 percent in the middle atmosphere following the silver iodide seeding. These small results suggest, however, that it may conceivably be possible to reduce the damage inflicted by hurricanes and possibly to influence the path followed by these storms. Because of the great potential value of these efforts, it is urgent that more realistic hurricane models be developed and that further careful field tests of model predictions be carried out.

Another advance deals with the dissipation of cool fog by seeding with dry ice, silver iodide, or liquid propane. An operational practice at many airports in the United States, the Soviet Union, and France, the rate of success appears to be about 75 percent. But, because cool fogs are only about 7 percent of the fogs occurring at airports in the United States, the new effort has been

A satellite's view of hurricanes in the Atlantic Ocean
and Caribbean. The white, fluffy masses forming
swirls are the hurricanes and part of the large storms
in the lower atmosphere.

directed at clearing warm fogs. Some successes have
been reported using a variety of means such as seeding
with very large pellets of dry ice, downwash from
helicopters, and exhaust from jet engines. But climatologists insist that there does not exist a proven, practical
method for the dissipation of warm fogs.

Climatologists and meteorologists also have made advances in hail suppression. Throughout the past decade,
there have been widespread efforts to prevent damage
caused by hailstorms. Large amounts of silver iodide have
been added to clouds to try to reduce the size of hailstones

Increasing amounts of smoke and dust, carbon dioxide, and heat are being introduced into the atmosphere by man's activities. All of these have some effect on weather. Today, there is approximately 12% more carbon dioxide in the atmosphere than before the turn of the century.

by increasing their number. Spectacular successes have been reported by scientists in Russia and China over a period of years in protecting crops from destruction by hail. In these experiments, seeding agents were introduced directly into the supercooled region of the clouds by rockets or artillery shells. The results of ice-nuclei seeding in other nations, including the United States, have been uncertain.

In spite of all the achievements made in weather and climate modification during the past five years, many problems still need to be worked out. Ray Davis, a University of Arizona law professor, argues that rainmaking, for example, must be considered a form of "cloud rustling" and believes that diverting another nation's or state's cloud system could be construed as an illegal diversion of its water. "If one nation causes environmental harm to another, there is definitely a liability," claims Davis. "I think weather modification can become a form of open warfare, enabling hostile countries to cause droughts or floods in the lands of their enemies."

The Dust Bowl of the 1930s is the type of disaster that farmers fear most. Despite all the predictions in 1977 that another one is due, there is ample evidence that the so-called
"20-year cycle" may not be real.

The long-term effects of weather modification might
be even more disastrous. For example, tropical storms
serve as an environmental safety valve, enabling the
earth to distribute the enormous heat which would otherwise build up around the equator. Hindering these storms
could drastically alter the earth's atmosphere and
climate, even for the worse. Scientists fear that altering
weather patterns over one region of the globe could result
in the disruption of rainfall and damage or even destroy
vital crops elsewhere.

A great deal of study has gone into the inadvertent
results of modification. During the beginning of the 1960s,
interest in the by-products of weather was limited to the
effect of the increasing carbon dioxide concentration and
temperature of the lower atmosphere. Conclusions were
variable and uncertain. During the 1970s, models have
been created which were more realistic than the earlier
ones. Calculations using those models indicated that the
expected increase of perhaps 20 percent in atmospheric
$CO_2$ by the year 1999 might result in a surface

The tornado is the most vicious and destructive of all small-
scale storms. Hundreds of people lose their lives because of
tornadoes each year, and many more are made homeless.
Often these storms strike with little or no warning, and the
public has little time to seek protection or get out of the
storm's way. Tornado funnels typically have a lifetime of a
few minutes to half an hour. They may vary in width from
10 to 1000 yards. Tornadoes often occur in groups; when
one funnel is observed, others may develop in the vicinity.

temperature increase of 0.5° C. Since this is about the
natural change of climate over thirty years, the $CO_2$ problem is unlikely to be critical during the next few years.
However, over longer periods, during which the carbon
dioxide concentration may continue to increase, the climatic effects may be very significant.

During the 1970s, the effects of particular matter on
radiation has also received a great deal of attention.
There has been evidence that over the past thirty years,
atmospheric turbidity in the northern hemisphere has increased measurably, while direct solar radiation has

decreased. Electrical conductivity measurements reflect a large increase in particle concentration over the north Atlantic during the past fifty years with no corresponding increase in the central Pacific. The impact of these changes in particle concentration on global temperature may be appreciable, although the sign of the temperature changes has not yet been determined.

Because all conclusions are still very tentative, more analysis needs to be undertaken. Further progress in weather modification will demand increased understanding of certain basic processes and improved measuring capabilities. The most critical technical problems deal with:

- microphysical processes
- cloud measurements
- clarification of cloud-seeding results
- correct hurricane and convective storm models
- observations of gases and particles.

The microphysical process associated with rain has been especially difficult to understand. Careful laboratory experiments have given scientists accurate information concerning this process, although many fundamental aspects are not understood. For example, the ways in which ice nuclei form are not fully understood. The way in which ice crystals multiply in clouds is still obscure, as well as the process of how electrical charges separate in clouds.

Reliable methods for measuring the properties of clouds are badly needed. Aircraft are now used for making some measurements; they are not yet sufficiently accurate or reliable. They must be further developed and tested. Existing techniques using radar and other remote sensors must be further refined in order to make the necessary measurements in regions of severe turbulence where planes cannot fly.

Scientists say that before they can have confidence

Lightning during a thunderstorm constitutes only
one-tenth of a thunderstorm's electrical activity.
Scientists do not fully understand the intricacies
of lighning's origins and its interactions with the
many other elements of thunderstorms.

in planning extensive cloud-seeding operations, further
clarification of cloud-seeding results must occur. In order
to determine the possibilities of beneficial modifications
of severe storm dynamics, it is important that the simple
models of hurricanes and convective storms which now
exist be developed into more realistic models.

In order to know what effects the global climate are
being produced by changes in concentration of various
gases and particles, scientists must accumulate accurate
global data on carbon dioxide and aerosol concentrations, electrical conductivity, and total solar radiation.
Such observations must be closely coordinated with programs of global observations.

### The Political Climate of Weather

Along with all the critical technical problems, there also
exist major administrative problems.

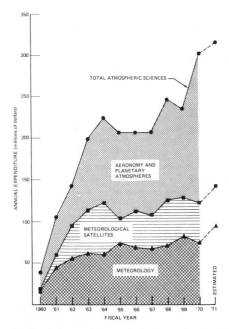

Federal expenditures for atmospheric-sciences research during the 1960s.

During the early years of the 1960s, the National Science Foundation was given the responsibility under Public Law 85-510 to "initiate and support a program of study, research, and evaluation in the field of weather modification and to report annually to the President and the Congress thereon." Under such an order, the government funds allocated by the National Science Foundation primarily to university scientists, was increased from $1.2 million per year at the beginning of the '60s to $3.3 million by 1971. During the same decade, an increase in funding of climate research took place in such federal agencies as the Departments of Interior, Commerce, and the Navy. The total annual budget supporting research in weather modification increased from $2.5 million in 1962 to $17 million in 1976.

In addition to support for basic research, these amounts include support for programs directed toward application of weather modification techniques. The Department of the Interior's Bureau of Reclamation has supported work directed at increasing water supply in the arid west; the Department of Agriculture has supported work directed at lightning suppression; the Navy, the National Aeronautics and Space Administration, and the Air Force have supported work geared to fog dispersal; and, the Navy and Commerce Departments have supported severe storm modification. Other agencies have supported similar applied objectives. Recognizing the broadened objectives of federal agency activities in weather modification, Congress passed in 1968 Public Law 90-407, which directed efforts toward a variety of agency missions in addition to scientific research and left to the executive branch the development of a coordinated program. As of today, there is no designated lead agency for weather modification.

This could be remedied by the designation of a federal agency responsible to the country for providing water supplies to cities or rural irrigation projects with the ability to predict the possible contribution of weather modification to its goal. This would obviously necessitate close contact between the agency and climatologists. It might also mean that the agency would have to carry out mission-oriented research projects on its own. If research convinces the federal agency of the value of weather modification, it should be responsible for stating its case for an operational program to the executive branch, Congress, and the public.

Today, some eleven separate agency programs exist for weather modification. Even the establishment of the National Oceanic and Atmospheric Administration (NOAA) has not solved the problem, because the major weather-modification programs still remain in the separate agencies. Despite widespread recognition of the need for stronger coordination in weather modification, the administrative problem of consolidation and coordination remains as one of the crucial blocks to a truly effective national weather modification program. Scientists feel that in order to solve the problem, the following requirements are necessary:

(1) Responsibility for research in weather modification must be closely associated with responsibility for research in the atmospheric sciences generally. The solution of important scientific problems in weather modification requires sophisticated understanding on a wide range of atmospheric processes.

(2) Agencies may have a legitimate need to conduct specific mission-oriented research and must be responsible for the development and support of these programs.

(3) National policy in weather modification must be based upon full consideration of relevant economic, social, ecological, and legal factors, as well as on scientific and technical factors.

The plea of scientists is for a suitable administrative solution which would assign lead responsibility for research in weather modification and for coordination of major field programs to a single agency. The agency would also encourage other agencies to continue to support programs within their specific areas of responsibility.

Problems of public policy issues are also monumental. Their questions have been the focus of study by several groups which have included lawyers, ecologists, economists, political scientists, statisticians, geographers, sociologists, as well as atmospheric scientists. The studies have attempted to answer such questions as: Is increased rain from extensive cloud seeding beneficial or harmful? Under what circumstances and to whom? Should the value of increased water supply outweigh the general public's desire for dry roads and more sunshine? What should receive top priority, water supply, transportation, or ecological considerations? Will the damages be irreparable or prove, over the long run, to be hazardous to our health? Obviously, each of these questions will have national, international, regional, as well as individual implications.

Naturally, there are no easy answers to these questions, interrelated as they are with many subjective elements. Scientists feel they will have to be coped with, rather than solved. Of all the questions raised, the three most crucial deal with aspects of the economy, law, and environment.

As far as economic aspects are concerned, there are many examples of projects for which attractive benefit-to-cost ratios are quite likely. These include augmenting water supplies for power generation and irrigation, reducing the occurrence of lightning-caused forest fires, increasing agricultural yield, and dispersing cold fog over highways and airports. Less certain technically, but potentially of the greatest economic value, would be the effect of reducing wind speeds associated with hurricanes and other severe storms.

In spite of all the benefits that may accrue, very little real effort has gone into evaluations of the economic feasibility of weather modification, especially in comparison with the large private expenditures which have been applied to operational cloud-seeding projects. The reasons, say scientists, include uncertainties in specifying the effects of an operation, the possible broad diffusion of benefits and losses beyond the specific industry or region intended, the difficulty in placing values on property damage and especially on loss of life, and the difficulty of assessing long-term effects.

Even in those cases where the economic value appears to be assured, the issues aren't so easy. For example, the costs of increasing rain in order to increase agricultural production must be compared with the costs of alternate methods of obtaining equivalent crop production increases. Such alternate methods would include crop diversification, selection of strains more resistant to drought, and shifting production to other locations, as well as creating other possible sources of water by means of desalting, reuse, or new dams. Economists feel that it is entirely possible that the benefit-to-cost ratio might be very different for the individual farmer, region, state, nation and world. Such economic evaluations, though important, would not dispose of the difficult public policy problems associated with weather modifications.

As far as the legal aspects are concerned, lawyers and scholars have been fascinated with the unusual questions posed by weather-modification operations. Already cases have come to trial in New York, Texas, Oklahoma, Nebraska, Pennsylvania, Washington, and California. In many of these instances, concern has revolved around who has the rights to clouds passing overhead. Obviously, clouds which pass over someone's land are potential assets that he may wish to put to profitable use, but does that person actually own the clouds? The question has not been answered. Analogies with laws regarding water supplies provided by streams, lakes, and wells have been argued, although these are really not very useful because of obvious differences between the two situations. New laws will have to be proposed which deal with the issues of:

(1) the right to use clouds over one's property
(2) the right to enjoy natural rain not modified by someone else's intervention
(3) the interest of the public in developing methods of effective weather modification
(4) the degree of liability incurred when damages are associated with deliberate weather modification.

Obviously, traditional procedures of law are not adequate to deal with the kinds of problems characteristic of weather control. Scientists feel that the development of the law should keep pace with scientific understanding and technical capability. It would be too soon to create a rigid legal structure controlling weather modification given the present knowledge deficiencies. The greatest need at this time is for legal provisions that will ensure scientists are able to carry out field research programs necessary to understand the processes associated with rain and the effects of deliberate modification. Scientists are in general agreement that because of the unity of the atmosphere, laws respecting weather modification should be the same across the country and, indeed, around the world. The primary responsibility for resolving the legal issues must lie with the federal government.

Even though most efforts at weather modification have concerned the seeding of clouds, the question is much broader than meets the eye. Among the ideas that have been mentioned are suppression of evaporation by coating water surfaces, melting ice by spreading carbon dust, raising temperature by growing dark-leaf ground cover, and glacial engineering designed to increase runoff from snow fields.

Of course, to these deliberate efforts at weather modification can be added less deliberate but significant examples of accidental modification such as the increase of carbon dioxide content in the atmosphere from fossil fuel burning, contribution to basic cloud formations from industrial and urban sources, and effects of added heat and particle matter to the atmosphere. Weather modification is part of the large group of major problems concerned with man's influence upon the environment. Public sensitivity to these problems has grown rapidly in the past few years. Climatologists feel that everyone must anticipate that as energy consumption increases and technology advances in the coming decades, more and more use will be made of the atmosphere and more efforts will be made to modify atmospheric processes. Environmental problems will not be solved and disposed of, they will have to be managed by people and institutions that combine a wide range of technical skills with an understanding of society's needs and desires.

In short, only government can be responsible for dealing with the range of problems intrinsic to weather control. The president and Congress must develop policy modifying, regulating, and controlling the weather. Obviously, these responsibilities require support of laboratory and field research, as well as professional investigations into the effects of modification on people, productivity, and ecology. Industry, because of its flexibility and innovative capacity, is best suited to develop operational techniques. Scientists feel, therefore, that Washington, D.C., should encourage industry to play the leading role in the exploitation of weather modification potentialities. They also argue America's universities are needed to contribute further scientific research and the development of public policy models. Universities can train the technicians and scientists needed for an effective national program, and maintain the research leadership essential to graduate training.

For instance, if and when hurricanes and other severe storms are to be modified and controlled, someone must be responsible for making operational decisions. Procedures will be needed for ensuring that programs fare in the fullest sense in the public interest. Before those programs are undertaken, there must be assurance that the operators are technically competent, all effects of the operation are known, all affected parties are represented in the decision-making process, and adequate provision established for liability in case of damages. A uniform system created by industry and the universities of licensing and mandatory reporting of operational procedures must be implemented.

The focus of responsibility for the overall direction of weather modification rests with Congress and the president. For example, what if international problems develop? Air cannot be confined within national boundaries. For instance, according to reports from Sweden, distinctly acidic rainfall in recent years may be responsible for the adverse effects on the forests of Scandinavia. Scientists are not certain of the acid source, although it probably originated from the industrial regions of western Europe and Sweden itself. As industrialization continues in the underdeveloped as well as developed nations, such damaging acid will multiply.

The international dimensions of the problems of weather modification demand more research to advance understanding of all the scientific and technical aspects. Discussions should be geared at obtaining international agreement on weather modification activities that could seriously affect the weather in regions beyond national borders. The more scientists learn about the world weather machine, the more they realize that it is an engine of enormous complexity. They are only beginning to figure out how it works or predict what it will do next. Although many feel that until we have a better understanding of the weather, we are wise not to tamper with it; scientists generally conclude that national planning and modification can take place now.

## The National Climatic Center

From all that has been said, it may seem that there are as many theories on climate as there are climatologists, and as many ways to guide the modification and control of weather. But everyone agrees on one point: scientists cannot yet predict climatic change with any guarantee. Additionally, everyone agrees that, first, climatic change moves in irregular cycles; second, we are living in one of the warmest periods of the past million years. A change of two degrees Celsius in the annual mean air temperature would have profound effects. Higher temperatures might expand arable land, but only if accompanied by increased rainfall. Warmth, as has been stated, might bring drier conditions. Lower temperatures could produce a climate generally wetter and less stable, one marked by storms, floods and freezes.

But thousands of Americans are seeking answers to their own questions which have not been answered by going to the records for their state's annual rainfall, average temperature, percentage of days with sunshine, and the mortality rate. Records are available at the National Oceanic and Atmospheric Administration's National Climatic Center. Located in western North Carolina at Asheville, the National Climatic Center is where thousands of serious seekers of climatological information are going for historical weather information and related products in the atmospheric sciences as well as aviation and agricultural information.

Before World War II, the science of climatology was a function of the country's weather services. Sporadic attempts at systematic weather records date back to the days of the Pilgrims when the Rev. John Companius conducted systematic observations of rainfall and weather conditions without the use of instruments in 1644 near Wilmington, Delaware. During the Colonial days, Washington, Franklin, and Jefferson took a more than casual interest in the weather. However, it was not until 1885 that official government interest was taken of the need for a systemized, nationwide record of climate in the United States. In 1890, the U.S. Weather Bureau was created as an agency of the Department of Agriculture and charged with "the taking of such meteorological observations as may be necessary to establish and record the climatic conditions of the United States."

The new Weather Bureau inherited almost 180 weather stations from the Army Signal Service (which carried out the government's weather programs before

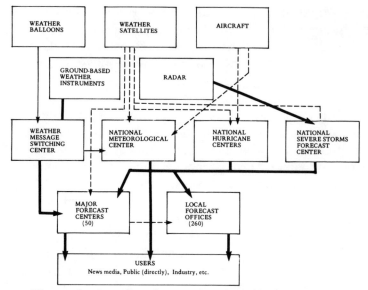

Thousands of weather observations taken daily by satellites, balloons, aircraft, ships, radar, and ground stations go into the making of nearly 2 million forecasts and warnings every year.

1890). The Bureau also received weather information for climate purposes from over 2,000 public-spirited citizens who volunteered to operate cooperative stations.

In contrast, the meteorological data for the United States today comes from over 12,000 voluntary observers, some 300 National Weather service facilities, numerous military installations, Federal Aviation Administration stations, and others. Additional information comes from environmental satellites, ships and buoys, automatic observing stations on land and at sea, and from foreign nations. The Environmental Data Service estimates more than 40 million observations are made throughout the world every year.

Looking over this early history, it is difficult to imagine how all these sightings and records could have been maintained in a useful form down through the years. Literally, tons and tons of paper containing raw data was

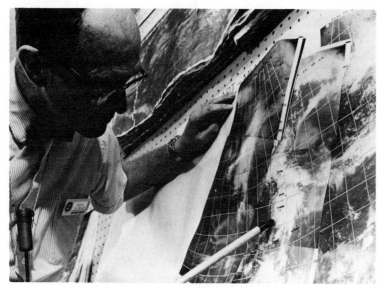

In this photograph, a weathercaster is analyzing
information in order to determine current weather
conditions and how the weather has changed over
the past few hours and days.

edited, analyzed, and published annually. An early solution to the problem of the sheer bulk of the records being
accumulated arrived with the punched data card method
of computer processing. Such data computer processing
methods were applied to the climatological data of the
decades since the '30s.

The sudden military demands of World War II lent
impetus to the full scale modernization of climatological
data processing techniques. Standard methods of observing and recording weather elements by the civil and
military meteorological services were devised. Machine
processing of weather information was then adapted in
all phases of climatology. The collection and storage of
weather records was centralized. In the meantime,
government officials were recognizing the value of global
procurement of weather information.

In 1951, the National Weather Records Center was established at Asheville, North Carolina. Over the next ten-year period, three other weather data processing facilities were consolidated because of the arrival of larger and more powerful computers. This new hardware enabled the quality control, summarization, and publication of climatological data to be accomplished more economically and efficiently at a single location. In 1965, the Environmental Data Service was formed, assuming many of the functions of the Weather Bureau. The facility's name was changed to the National Climatic Center in 1970.

Today, automation is the watchword at the center, where the amount and complexity of data reaches staggering quantities. Log sheets, recorder charts, radar photographs, satellite readouts, etc., pour in for processing, checking, publication, and archiving. Data is received by mail, and whether in manuscript form, on punched paper tape or on non-standard magnetic tape, is converted to magnetic tape. When the data is determined to be as error-free as possible, the tapes are used to produce a properly formatted microfilm image containing the required information, headings, column lines, and other material. These microfilm frames are then enlarged to page-size negatives for printing by photo offset methods. From all this, some 35 million pages of weather data bulletins are printed each year.

For the serious seeker of climatological information, data formerly contained on over one-half billion punched cards is now available on magnetic tape. Foreign meteorological services are sending their magnetic tapes to this growing collection as part of an exchange program. Data collected by satellites, in both film and magnetic tape, have added tremendously to the volume of environmental data reaching the center for archiving. This volume is increasing as more satellites are being flown. A special unit, the Satellite Data Services Branch, has been established to devote full attention to managing the ever-growing satellite data bank.

The National Climatic Center estimates that nearly half its total effort, beyond gathering, processing, and archiving data, is spent responding to requests from researchers, industry, commerce, and others. The center is not merely a vast repository of meteorological records; there are thousands of feet of shelf length holding the original manuscript, observational forms and autographic traces created at government weather stations and cooperative observers since the systematic collection of meteorological data began—literally trillions of weather and climate measurements.

The center also carries out highly involved climatological investigations. These studies require tabulations and summaries of climate data. Interpretations of the results are applied to specific problems presented by components of the National Oceanic and Atmospheric Administration. Included in this category are studies for the Federal Aviation Administration on high-altitude environmental conditions which might affect supersonic aircraft; wind speed for the National Aeronautics and Space Administration for planning where a rocket might be deflected from its planned path as it rises through the atmosphere; and, methods for analyzing air pollution potentials for the Environmental Protection Agency.

Thus, whatever information the National Climatic Center brings in, it distributes. In one form or another, a million copies of monthly and annual climatological publications are mailed out. Also, more than 100,000 questions from the general public are answered yearly.

# V

## Future Climates:
## Worldwide Weather Watches

*Even if we stop polluting with carbon dioxide today, its effect will be with us a very long time. I believe that within fifty years we'll discover how to modify large-scale climate. We're going to have to work in harmony with nature, not try to overpower her by brute force.*

J. Murray Mitchell, Jr.

In the spring of 1978, the most detailed analysis of the earth's atmosphere ever conducted began. Back in 1974, electronic eyes and ears were glued to a 20 million square mile patch of the equatorial region as some seventy nations took part in the Atlantic Tropical Experiment. That success in monitoring weather systems has now paved the way for a similar study of the entire planet in 1978. At that time, surface stations, ships, planes, buoys, balloons, rockets, and satellites will attempt to follow air and moisture movements and temperature variations over every region of the globe's surface during a twenty-four-month period. The project will be a segment of the United Nations Global Atmospheric Research Program (GARP). From this first GARP global experiment will, hopefully, come models for a clearer insight into weather developments, as well as reasons for longer-term climatic change.

Such a comprehensive international analysis is eagerly awaited by atmospheric scientists all over the world in order to clarify the overall picture of past climatic changes in terms of future trends. For a long time, scientists have known of the existence of large-scale fluctuations that have taken place over a very long time period and the concurrent existence of random fluctuations presumed to exist on all time scales. For instance, in addition to the dominant period of some 100,000 years, there have been smaller periodic fluctuations with time scales of about 2,500 years, and shorter period fluctuations of 100 to 400 years. No periodic time scale of climatic change in terms of decades has yet been clearly defined.

As for determining what future climates might be like, some inferences from past climate behavior can be made. It should be understood, however, that because of the limited ability of virtually all climatic indicators, especially those for the relatively remote geological past, it is most difficult to determine whether the apparent fluctuations are predictably periodic, and/or whether they are due to basic changes not yet fully understood. In the case of the longer-period variations (100,000-year to 20,000-year periods), there is strong circumstantial evidence to suggest that these may have been caused by changes of the earth's orbit, which are now known to vary the seasonal and latitudinal distribution of solar radiation received at the top of the atmosphere. In other cases, the observed variations have yet to be convincingly related to any external climatic control. Scientists caution that the mere existence of such variations does not necessarily mean that changes in the external boundary conditions are involved. The internal dynamics of the climatic system itself may well be the root of some of the features. Whether forced or not, climatic behavior of this type will be receiving the full attention of GARP's careful two-year study, since the conclusions gleaned will bear directly upon the problem of inferring the future climate.

The prediction of climate is clearly an enormously complex problem. Although scientists have no useful skill in predicting weather beyond a few weeks into the future, there is an urgent need to predict the climate for years, decades, and even centuries ahead. Not only do we have to consider the complex year-to-year changes possibly induced by the internal dynamics of the climatic system, and the probable continuation of the unexplained periodic and episodic fluctuations of the last few thousand years, but also the changes caused by less predictable factors such as aerosols, SST emissions, and volcanic eruptions.

In the face of so many uncertainties, any projections of what our climate will be like in the future is little better than a guess. Nevertheless, scientists are speculating about the possible cause of global climate in the decades and centuries immediately ahead by making certain assumptions about the character of the major fluctuations noted in the climatic records.

First of all, studies suggest that the contributions of the longer-period fluctuations to present-day climatic change are very minor. Scientists feel it is next to impossible for longer-period fluctuations to contribute substantially to the changes of climate taking place in the twentieth century. If the long-period fluctuations of climate are those that bring on ice ages or cause them to recede, it would seem that the transition into the next glacial period (even if it has already started) would take many hundreds or thousands of years before a major shift from present climatic conditions occurs.

Second, the scientist's ability to anticipate local patterns of climate changes is limited. For instance, analysis has shown that while the northern hemisphere average air temperatures rose only 0.2° C during the 1899 to 1939 period, there were many areas which deviated sharply from the hemispheric average. Certain areas in part of the United States showed a 1° C rise in average temperature (six times the average), parts of Scandinavia and Mexico exhibited temperature increases of 2° C (twelve times the hemispheric average), while in frigid Spitsbergen, the warming was 5° C (twenty-five times the average).

Third, a minority of scientists conclude there is a likelihood of a major deterioration of global climate during the decades ahead. Climatologists say that whether climatic fluctuations are or are not periodic, those which are most relevant for global climate in the years and decades ahead are the shorter-period fluctuations and not the longer-period changes. But even if the phase of the longer-period changes is such as to contribute to a cooling of today's climate, the contribution of such fluctuations to the rate of change of present-day climate would seem to be overwhelmed by the greater impact of the short period fluctuations.

Atmospheric scientists are often asked when the present interglacial period will end. Paleoclimatologists agree that the most important warm periods (interglacials) which have followed each of the conclusions of the major glaciations have had durations of approximately 12,000 years. In every case, a period of considerably colder climate has followed an interglacial interval. Since some 11,000 years have elapsed since the onset of the present period of prominent warmth, whether we are indeed on the brink of colder climate no one can yet answer. To many scientists, there seems little doubt that the present period of unusual warmth will eventually give way to a time of colder climate. Some experts feel that as each hundred years passes, there is a 7 percent greater chance of meeting its beginning. On the other hand, some experts feel that the climate might decline gradually over a period of thousands of years. There is, however, no consensus in terms of the magnitude or rate of the transition. The beginning of this climatic decline could be several thousand years away, although there is an outside chance that a serious worldwide cooling could grip the planet within the next one hundred years.

What is the nature of the climatic changes following the end of a period of interglacial warmth? From intensive studies of soils and sediments, scientists discovered that major changes in vegetation always took place at the end of the previous interglacial period. Deciduous forests that covered areas during the major glaciations were replaced by sparse shrubs. Huge dust storms swirled at will. Agricultural productivity was marginal at best. Scientists have discovered that the stratification of fossil pollen deposits in eastern Macedonia clearly demonstrates a marked change in vegetative cover between interglacial warmth and the following cold centuries. Forests of oak and pine that flourished in the area diminished to fields of shrub. Grass was the dominant plant cover. Evidence from deep sea cores shows a major change in the surface water temperature in the north Atlantic between interglacial and glacial periods, and marine sediment data shows that the magnitude of the changes that took place during abrupt glacial cooling was about half the total glacial to interglacial change itself.

Yet all these projections could be superceded by an entirely different future climate due to man's accidental or intentional interference with otherwise natural variation. Atmospheric $CO_2$ is diminishing, which means atmospheric concentrations must increase over the long term. Aerosols and the releasing of waste heat may combine to offset the future natural cooling trend and to enhance a natural warming. Such happenings serve to illustrate the unknowns carried into the problems of future climatic changes by the inadvertent interference of man in taking action before adequate information is gathered on the natural variations.

## A Climatic Research Program

As the current use of land for agriculture, the use of water supplies for irrigation and drinking, and the use of both airsheds and watersheds for waste disposal approach their limits, it becomes obvious that if a change of climate occurs for only a few years' time, it could cripple our use of these resources. No one can predict the devastating effects it would have on the economy and mankind. Scientists realize all too clearly that although past climatic changes have had a profound effect on our activities, future changes will have even greater impact.

All agree that if we are to react rationally to inevitable future climatic changes, and competently predict their future course (whether natural or man-induced), a far greater understanding of those changes is needed. The mechanics of the climatic system are so complex and scientific observation of its behavior is so incomplete, no one knows for sure what triggers any particular change.

Therefore, atmospheric and earth scientists across the nation are recommending that an integrated national research program be created which will contain the observational, analytical, and research components necessary to achieve this understanding. During the past years, pieces of the climatic mosaic have been considered in relative isolation from each other, a method of subdivision which is not natural to the traditional scientific method. But now, scientists insist, the time has arrived to plan and execute a broad and coordinated attack on the problems of climate and weather. Such a national climatic research program would not stifle the creation of new and independent lines of attack, nor seek to assemble all

| Variable or Index | Method | Coverage | Effort Required * | Frequency Required ** |
|---|---|---|---|---|
| *Atmospheric indices* | | | | |
| Solar constant | Satellite | Global | N | W |
| Absorbed radiation, albedo | Satellite | Global | P | W |
| Latent heating | Satellite | Global | N | W |
| Surface latent heat flux | Satellite | World ocean | N | W |
| Surface sensible heat flux | Satellite | Regional | N | W |
| Cloudiness | Satellite | Global | P | W |
| Surface wind over ocean | Radar scattering | World ocean | N | W |
| *Oceanic indices* | | | | |
| Sea-surface temperature | Ships, satellites, buoys | World ocean | E | W |
| Surface-layer heat storage | XBT, AXBT, buoys | Mid-latitude and low-latitude oceans | E,N | W |
| Heat transport | Moored buoys | Selected sections | N | W |
| Temperature structure | Ships | Selected sections | E | S |
| Surface salinity | Ships, buoys | High latitudes | E | W |
| Sea level | Tide gauges | Selected coastal and island sites | E | W |
| Composition, dissolved gases | Conventional sampling | Selected sections | E | S |
| *Cryospheric indices* | | | | |
| Floating ice extent | Satellite | Polar seas, lakes | E | M |
| Ice-sheet budget parameters | Satellite | Greenland, Antarctica | N | Y |
| Mountain glacier extent | Satellite | Selected sites | E | Y |
| Snow cover | Satellite | Continents | E | M |
| *Surface and hydrologic indices* | | | | |
| River discharge | Flow gauges | Selected sites | E, N | W |
| Soil moisture | Satellite | Land areas | E | W |
| Lake levels | Gauges | Selected sites | E | W |
| Precipitation | Satellite, radar, gauges | Global | E | W |
| *Composition and turbidity indices* | | | | |
| Chemical composition | Sampling | Selected sites | E | S |
| Aerosols and dust | Satellite | Global | E | W |
| *Anthropogenic indices* | | | | |
| Thermal pollution | Sampling | Continents and coasts | N | W |
| Air and water pollution | Sampling | Global | E | W |
| Land use | Satellite | Continents | E | Y |

\* N, completely new monitoring effort required; E, expansion of present monitoring efforts required;
P, present (or slightly expanded) monitoring efforts satisfactory but coordination and further analysis required.

\*\* W, weekly (or possibly daily in some cases); M, monthly; S, seasonally; Y, yearly (or possibly decadal in some cases).

## Climatic Research

efforts under a single authority. Its purpose would be to provide a coordinating framework for the necessary research on all major aspects of the problems, as well as the establishment of new ideas, theories, and efforts.

Specifically, then, what precise climatic events and processes have been identified as subjects for study under such a program?

The major characteristics of climatic changes during the past twenty years include all the present season and annual circulation abnormalities over many large regions of the earth (i.e., droughts in China and the Pacific west coast; severe freezes in Europe and New York), along

This weather satellite system (ITOS) has the capacity
of achieving global observation on a daily basis. The
artists's conception illustrates the satellite in its mission
mode, with its solar proton sensors extended.

with some longer-term trends. Satellite observations in
1977 have charted changes in worldwide cloudiness,
snow cover, and the global radiation balance. Also, from
analysis of selected paleoclimatic data, scientists have
discovered that ancient climates have been somewhat the
same in behavior as our present-day weather. This new
information also verifies the presence of the 100,000-year
climatic fluctuation associated with the earth's major
glaciations.

From the analysis of a variety of climate models, as
well as from the study of recent weather information,
scientists can now identify a number of links or processes

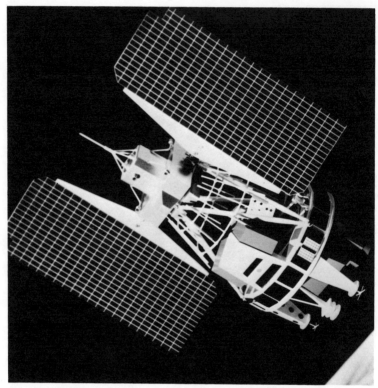

Artist's concept of the Earth Resources Technology
Satellite.

in the phenomenon of climatic change. On at least the
shorter time scales, the climatic system is regulated by a
series of feedback mechanisms, especially those involving
cloudiness, surface temperature, and surface albedo.
Underlying these effects is the increasing evidence that
large-scale thermal interactions between the ocean and
atmosphere are the most important components in
weather variations on time scales from months to
thousands of years. Therefore, it is imperative that these
interactions must be thoroughly analyzed. Scientists feel
that the role of the oceans in the climatic systems raises
the possibility of some degree of useful predictability on

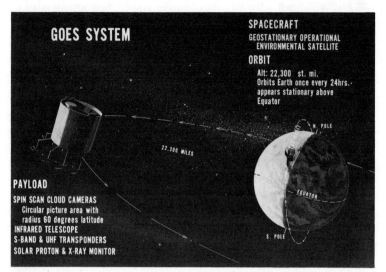

GOES, the Geostationary Operational Environmental Satellite, is one of the most sophisticated weather satellites ever conceived. These geostationary satellites are positioned in a fixed location 22,300 miles above the earth. The United States now operates two GOES systems, one centered over Colombia, South America (70° west longitude) and the other over the mid-Pacific (135° west longitude). The special photographic and infrared (heat) measurements made by GOES are important because they provide weathercasters with current, accurate, and meaningful information. Each GOES system looks down on nearly one-quarter of the earth's surface and can provide comprehensive picture coverage every 30 minutes. Thus, weathercasters can track the development and movement of severe weather systems, particularly over the oceans where surface data are usually sparse.

annual time scales and is thus a crucial subject for further research.

But, even though these identifiable processes represent significant discoveries, they are nonetheless concerned with separate pieces of the problem. What scientists say they cannot identify at the present time is exactly how the total climatic system operates. Little is really known of its most critical and sensitive parts, which processes are responsible for its changes, and what are the most likely future climates. In essence, while we know something about climate itself, we know almost nothing about climatic change.

What the scientists do know are the important problems requiring serious and careful investigation. These concern the design and creation of improved climatic models of the ocean and atmosphere, new observations and the further analysis of old discoveries and problems, and the simulation of climatic variations under a variety of conditions for the past, present, and future. As scientists attempt to research these areas on a global scale, it becomes very important that there is ensured the smooth flow of data and ideas, as well as of resources, among all parts of the problem. The effort given by each nation (and internationally through GARP) to the improvement of weather forecasting must also be given to a program devoted to climatic variation—a problem whose global implications are even more serious and the physical basis for change is not at all well understood.

Experts say that other circumstances also demand that a major research program on climatic change be initiated immediately. For example, during the past few years, scientists have had available to them an unprecedented amount of meteorological satellite observational hardware. Because of this new strength, initial observations of the cloudiness, radiation budget and albedo have increased to include the vertical distribution of moisture and temperature, the extent of ice and snow, the sea surface temperature, presence of particles, as well as the character of the land surface. This new and regular global coverage offered by such satellites is clearly an observational breakthrough previously unachieved.

The steady increase in the capacity and speed of computers that has occurred since their introduction during the late 1940s has reached the point where numerical integration of global circulation models over many months or even years is now practical. Atmospheric scientists feel that such calculations, coupled with the associated data processing, will be the foundation of climatic research for decades to come.

The recent development of new models of the inter-action between ocean and atmosphere is also a break-through of the early 1970s. Simulation of climatic varia-tion with these new model theories is just commencing.

To climatologists the world over, these break-throughs indicate that the time has arrived during which progress is in proportion to the efforts made. By coordi-nating all the efforts into a coherent research program, scientists expect to achieve great insights into climatic variation.

In order to more effectively create a national climatic research program, atmospheric scientists have recommended a specific series of steps for research as well as application of the data gathered. In terms of the information needed for climate analysis and research, a worldwide inventory of climatic data should be organized to determine the amount, nature, and location of past and present instrumental observations of a number of variables. Those variables include surface pressure, temperature, humidity, wind, rainfall, snowfall, and cloudiness, upper-air temperature, pressure-altitude, wind, ocean temperature, salinity, current, the location and depth of land ice, sea ice, and snow, as well as the surface insulation, ground temperature, ground moisture, and runoff. All this information would then be used to systematically compute a basic set of climatic statistics for as many time periods and for as many regions of the world as possible. These should include the means, the variances, and the extremes for monthly, seasonal, an-nual, and decadal periods for both individual nations as well as the entire planet.

Scientists, however, stress the great opportunity available in the potentially unmatched coverage by obser-vations from satellites. Those that are of climatic value should be systematically catalogued, summarized, and made available on as timely a basis as possible. Current-ly, available summaries of such data are providing scien-tists with important new results. In the establishment of a national climatic index monitoring program, scientists urge that an organized effort be made to locate, classify, and summarize information from the following sources:

(A)    historical sources such as books, manuscripts, logs, and journals during the past five hundred years

(B)    proxy data from tree-ring growth patterns, glacier movements, lake and deep-sea sediments, ice cores, and studies of soil

(C)    studies of chemical properties of tree rings, polar ice caps, ocean sediments, and pollen records

(D)    the last 30,000 years, an interval dominated by the waxing and waning of continental ice sheets

(E)    the last 150,000 years, an interval including the last period in the climate history of the earth which was evidently much like the one today

(F)    the last 1,000,000 years and beyond, an opportunity to compare the circulation pat-terns which have characterized the last several full-glacial and interglacial periods

(G)    marine sediment cores, beneath the ocean's floor to a mile

(H)    Antarctic ice sheet records

(I)    atmospheric indices, monitoring of the atmosphere's heat balance

(J)    oceanic indices, monitoring those oceanic variables associated with large-scale thermal interaction with the atmosphere

(K)    cryospheric indices, monitoring the influence of snow and ice cover on the surface energy balance

(L)    surface and hydrologic indices, monitoring the
       natural changes of vegetative cover, soil
       moisture and ground water, discharge of ma-
       jor river systems, water balance of the world's
       huge lakes, and rainfall over the oceans
(M)    composition and turbidity indices, monitoring
       the role which atmospheric particles and
       aerosols play in the heat balance of the at-
       mosphere
(N)    Anthropogenic indices, monitoring man's
       increasing interference with the environment
       (waste, thermal discharges of power generat-
       ing and industrial facilities, chemical pollu-
       tion, forest clearing, irrigation and urbaniza-
       tion)

A summary of all the elements atmospheric scientists recommend for a national climatic research program are listed below. As yet, scientists have not assessed the required accuracy of the various monitored indices, nor have they thoroughly analyzed the capability of the present available instrumentation. They are the first to admit that further analysis is required to determine the characteristic variability of each climatic index. At least twenty years are required for the monitoring activity in order to assemble a meaningful body of information for analysis. All these efforts should be planned and coordinated on not only the national scale, but also as part of an international climatic program.

While these research recommendations are carried out, an additional segment of study is required to determine applications of the climatic studies (and especially of climate models). Scientists contend that it is precisely in these applications that the program would achieve its maturity. If serious attention to them is delayed until man's understanding is complete or the models created are perfect, they may never be undertaken. With scientific caution, climatologists feel the time has come for a vigorous attack on the following areas of climate model application:

- simulation of the earth's climatic history
- explorations of possible future climates
- development of long-range or climatic forecasting
- assessment of climate's impact on human beings, food, and energy, and
- social and economic impacts.

# VI

# What's the Forecast?

What was termed the "worst drought-winter-drought in the past century" was causing a severe strain on the financial resources of the nation during 1976-1977. Costs of relief were skyrocketing across America, eroding the budgets of thousands of communities and casting thousands of farmers into struggles for economic survival. Two-thirds of the country's 3000-odd counties were placed on the federal emergency drought impact list, making them eligible for emergency funds.

By the fall of 1977, 41 of the 48 contiguous states were suffering from moderate to severe drought. Glen Loomis, who coordinates the emergency relief effort within the Department of Agriculture, said:

> It's been alarming how widespread the drought has been. It's the worst in the history of the nation in terms of total geographic extent and severity. We have not had as much resource damage like soil blown away and erosion as in the 1930s, partly because of conservation measures undertaken since then. But a lot of people cannot understand how the drought can be so bad

when we're forecasting near-record grain crops . . .
Believe me, the overall impact, both short and long-
term, is going to be severe.

The drought's effects have been as diverse as they are
widespread. Despite intermittent rains during the summer of 1977, most of the nation's forests and grazing
lands were labeled tinderboxes ready to ignite with the
first careless match. Ranchers had to sell off their herds
because many public grazing lands were declared off
limits. In forests and fields, insect populations grew enormously. Municipal water wells in hundreds of midwestern towns could not longer supply daily water needs. In
large cities, water mains were breaking as the ground
shrank from moisture loss.

Furthermore, some 300,000 workers were laid off
their jobs nationwide because of drought or severe win-
ter-induced energy curtailments. Fisheries in the northwest and southeast suffered as spawning streams dried
up, thereby throwing thousands of other workers out of
work.

Is our climate changing for the worst?

Virtually all climatologists agree that throughout geological history the normal climate of the globe was so
warm that subtropical weather reached 65° F north and
south and there was almost a total absence of polar ice.
But it's only been less than one half of one percent of the
earth's history that glaciers from the polar areas touched
the temperate zones of the northern hemisphere. The latest such advance, which began over a million years ago,
was highlighted by incredible geological upheavals and
the birth of man. During those times, huge ice sheets advanced and retreated over the continents, the last retreat
taking place some 35,000 years ago.

Within recorded history there have been small glacial advances and retreats. Alpine passes now covered
with ice were used from A.D. 500 to 700. From Greenland,

ships sailed through passages now blocked by ice floes. Furthermore, from A.D. 800-1400, there were flourishing communities in now-barren Greenland. Gradually, cooling of the climate forced their abandonment around A.D. 900.

Can the earth be warming? As we know, a 2° F increase in the earth's overall temperature would clear the polar seas of all ice. Yet, as of the fall of 1977, in parts of western North America, glaciers were observed advancing, while eastern North America seemed to be warming. Scientists have had routine temperature measurements for over one hundred years. But these have not been too reliable, because of changes in instruments and methods of observation.

Perhaps the only real conclusion to be drawn about our climate is that scientists do not know whether it is changing drastically. Geologically, mankind may be at the end of the ice age, or may just be having a breathing spell of a few centuries before the next advance of the glaciers. The nation's foremost climate experts agree that they can't yet come up with a reliable long-range weather forecast which can predict such an event. However, these scientists also agree that with a few more millions of dollars in research funds they just might be able to achieve a reliable long-range weather forecast—in less than a decade.

Jerome Namias, a research meteorologist at the University of California's Scripps Institute of Oceanography, says that recent advances in atmospheric physics, global satellite surveillance, and computer modelling have sharpened the predictive capacity of meteorologists so they do a pretty fair job on tomorrow's weather picture— and even next week's.

But what's needed to have forecasts that will be valid a month or a crop season ahead is a new research push that exploits every clue from lake-bottom sediments and tree rings to sunspot observations and sea surface temperatures that portend day-by-day shifts.

Dr. J. Murray Mitchell, Jr., senior research climatologist for NOAA's Environmental Data Service, a scientist whose expertise is held in the highest esteem by colleagues the world over, feels that the recent weather extremes on both sides of the United States are part of a cycle which fluctuates every twenty to twenty-two years. Sunspot activity is nearly at a minimum right now, and that too fluctuates on a similar cycle, although the reasons for the connection are wholly obscure. According to Mitchell, the twenty-year climate cycle doesn't tell you when a drought will hit, or where it will hit, or how hard it will hit. It only offers a clue that a drought is coming. During 1977, the Pacific west coast was at the highest-risk part of the cycle. California, for example, could continue in another year of drought, or could receive a wet winter.

This is why Mitchell, Namias, and other scientists were asking Congress to pass a "National Climate Program." The proposed program, financed from $16 to $50 million during its first year, would monitor the earth's climate trends, analyze economic and social impacts, improve techniques for long-range forecasting and train large numbers of new weather scientists. Says Mitchell:

> If the future tendency of the world's climate is in doubt, and if mankind must depend upon accurate information about changing weather trends in order to plan his affairs wisely, climatologists must then organize and implement appropriate research programs in terms of necessary facilities, support, and desirable timetables, for both short-range and long-range phases. Not only this, but climatologists should take a careful look at themselves in order to determine how well they are responding to the challenge of assessing climate's future realistically, responsibly, and objectively.

Indeed, atmospheric experts such as Mitchell and Namias feel that among the wrongs committed by their profession is the myopic way in which climatologists have been looking at the statistics of past climates. Scientists have been too quick in extrapolating "data" of climatic variability from limited past experiences. Some have been looking at a thirty-year cooling trend in northern hemispheric average temperature and reported that the climate in the hemisphere is cooling at the present time. (One recent study suggested the cooling has already bottomed out, if not actually reversed.) Also, a few scientists have looked at a five-year record of density-weighted mean hemispheric temperature, plus a five-year record of the extent of ice and snow cover in the Arctic, and, discovering trends in both, have issued bulletins that mankind is approaching disaster. Recent data in both instances shows the "trends" as temporary excursions of climate which have since reversed themselves. Similarly, the tragic droughts in western Africa's Sahel zone has, according to some scientists, an irreversible effect of global atmospheric pollution. Though that drought is now over, pollution continues. Says Dr. Mitchell,

> We have tended to focus on developing climate disturbances as "the problem" of climate, as we did at the time of the Sahelian drought. We have seemed to forget in our preoccupation with the crisis of the moment that all climate-bred disasters are essentially only chance realizations of a much broader class of climatic variability which is the more meaningful object of our concerns. I would venture to say that the world will experience innumerable climatic crises of other kinds and in other parts of the world, before it is time for the Sahel to be ravaged by another, similar drought a few decades hence.

Another irresponsible and myopic way of announcing climate change, say the experts, is the one-dimensional manner many climatologists have used to explain the various weather flukes and disturbances. For example, scientists have tended to pick out one, or even a few simplistic causative mechanisms to account for the facts of past climatic change, and to rely on these as a guide to future climatic developments. Actually, there are undoubtedly numerous causative mechanisms, some internal and some external to the climate system, which govern weather change and climatic variability. Certainly no mechanism can be realistically dealt with in isolation from the others. All have to be considered together in a suitable general physical framework before scientists can truly understand climatic changes.

Thus, because climatologists do not yet have an intelligent grasp of all the causative mechanisms, nor are they yet certain what actually constitutes a suitably general physical framework to encompass those mechanisms, it is inaccurate for anyone to say he can explain the changes of global average temperature during the past century as the result of increasing atmospheric pollution, or of changing solar activity.

Experts feel that where interesting statistical relationships appear to exist—for instance, between climatic variations and such plausible forcing phenomena as volcanic eruptions, carbon dioxide trends, or sunspot numbers—they must be reported only as possible clues to climatic behavior. Then, and only then, can hypotheses to account for weather changes be offered for study. But these must be recognized for what they really are: statistical relationships and hypotheses. They are not self-sufficient explanations of climate behavior and reliable bases for climate predictions.

In spite of these very human types of overreaction, climatologists can be very satisfied with the things they are doing right. For example, they are discovering the value of extending climatic records into the past as far as they can and in as much detail as scientific advances allow. Where these meteorological records and human recordings begin to fail (around two centuries), scientists are slowly reconstructing climate's chronology during earlier millennia by means of a number of "proxy" indicators such as tree rings, deep sediment analyses, pollen profiles, variations in ice cores, etc. Such analyses allow scientists to place climatic experiences into more accurate historical perspectives. It turns out that the seemingly one-of-a-kind climatic developments seen in current meteorological records have numerous historical precedents. Because of this, say the experts, more realistic bounds on climatic behavior can be established, resulting in a more confident and realistic assessment, and more reliable assessments can be made of the causative factors in climatic change.

Other promising developments include the discovery of modern technological tools equal to the task of developing comprehensive numerical models of climate behavior. Scientists are turning more than ever before to climate modeling as a means for focusing on all the factors likely to account for climate variability and change. In this manner do scientists hope to clarify the limits of predictability and to focus research on those aspects of atmospheric behavior which promise to be predictable for decades ahead.

Climatologists are dramatically broadening their capacity to monitor the terrestrial and extraterrestrial environment through remote sensing technology and a variety of new satellite observing systems to track all manners of environmental variation that would trigger climatic variability. Adds Dr. Mitchell,

> All of these promising developments will eventually come together to provide a sound basis for assessing our future climate. That day cannot come soon enough. For the present, we must settle for vague, qualitative judments as to what the future is more likely to bring.

The world may have to prepare itself for the breakdown of the interglacial warmth of the past 8,000 years, and begin the transition into a colder, more glacial regime. The onset of that transition is an unknown number of centuries or millennia away. Conceivably, it has happened already. We may assume that any such transition, whether past or future, would proceed so slowly as to be barely perceptible in a human lifetime and well-disguised amid the more rapid fluctuations of climate, of an irregular and transient character, that seem always to be with us. Meanwhile, man is beginning to have appreciable impacts on the climate, mostly as it appears now in the direction of warming. These impacts are likely to grow in importance in future decades and centuries. The resulting picture of future climatic developments is contradictory and very unclear. Let us get on, as soon as we can, with the mammoth research task that is plainly required to clarify that picture.

The mechanisms for researching climatic information and getting it to those who need it most revolve around a national program with a number of components or subprograms. Each subprogram would be responsible for a specific portion of the overall effort. For example, perhaps the three most crucial divisions of effort for the practical execution of a program would be:

A *Climatic Data-Analysis Unit (CDAP)*: Scientists feel that in order to promote the extensive assembly and analysis of climatic information a Climatic Data-Analysis Program (CDAP) be created as a major subprogram of the national research program. Such a program would facilitate the exchange of information among the various climatic data depositories and research projects, as well as to support the coordinated preparation, analysis, and distribution of appropriate climatic statistics.

*Climatic Index Monitoring Program (CIMP):* Also recommended by scientists, this would promote the monitoring of the various climatic indices. It would support and coordinate the collection of data on selected climatic indices and ensure their systematic dissemination on a timely and sustained basis.

*Climatic Modeling and Applications Program (CMAP):* Finally, scientists urge this program be created in order to promote the construction and application of the various new climatic models. The purpose of this unit would be to support necessary background scientific research, as well as to ensure the systematic application of appropriate models to the problems of climatic reconstruction, prediction and impact.

Once Congress and the president decide to fund a national climatic research program, climatologists recommend the following immediate and subsequent objectives:

| Subprogram | Immediate Objectives 1977-1979 | Subsequent Objectives |
|---|---|---|
| Climatic data analysis (CDAP) | 1. Development of climatic data analysis facilities | 1. Development of global climatic data-analysis system |
| | 2. Statistical analysis of climatic variability, predictability, feedback processes | 2. Assembly and processing of global climatic data, (conventional, satellite, historical, proxy data) |
| | 3. Statistical climatic-impact studies (crops, human affairs) | 3. Development of climatic impact models |
| Climatic index monitoring (CIMP) | 1. Monitoring of oceanic mixed layer | 1. Satellite monitoring of global heat-balance components |
| | 2. Monitoring of ice, snow, and cloud cover | 2. Monitoring selected physical processes |

| Climatic modeling and applications (CMAP) | 3. Expansion of proxy data sources<br>4. Monitoring system simulation studies | 3. Development of global climatic index monitoring system |
|---|---|---|
| | 1. Development of oceanic mixed-layer models | 1. Development of fully coupled atmosphere-ocean-ice models |
| | 2. Development and analysis of provisionally coupled models (sensitivity, predictability studies) | 2. Development of statistical-dynamical climate models |
| | 3. Development of simplified climatic models and related theoretical studies | 3. Parameterization of mesoscale processes, similation of climatic feedback mechanisms |
| | 4. Selected paleoclimatic reconstructions | 4. Experimental seasonal climatic forecasts by dynamical models |

The long-range goals and full-scale operations of a proposed national climate research program in the decades beyond 1980 are diagramed above. Climatologists hope that during these years the full interaction among the observational, analysis, modeling, and theoretical components of the program will develop, leading to the development of an effective global climatic data system and to a general consensus regarding the reasons for climatic variation.

Although such long-range goals and priorities cannot really be set for such a long period, experts insist that the eventual practical payoffs will be the determination of the degree to which climatic variations on seasonal, annual, decadal, and longer times scales may be predicted and the degree to which they may be controlled by man.

There was a time not so very long ago when atmospheric scientists perceived the problem of climatic change as having primarily to do with the ice ages of the remote past. After all, the present-day climate wasn't supposed to be changing. Generally, when new information was published which suggested that climate was changing (such as a long meteorological record with a trend in it), scientists would conclude that something wrong with the definition of climate.

Today, climate change means something entirely different. Climate is no longer defined as static, but dynamic. Scientists now accept as ordinary climatic change in a single generation or less. Today's current trend of big freezes and droughts finds itself the focus of animated discussion on television, in the daily newspapers, in high government circles, and in scientific forums.

Why has this sudden change of perspective on climate change occurred? Is the climate itself behaving unusually, something it has never done before?

According to Dr. J. Murray Mitchell, "Not really. True, the climate is now seen as inherently variable, whereas it was not seen that way before. But the climate is not suddenly becoming variable in a way that it had never been variable before."

In terms of why climatic change has burst into public consciousness as a matter of vital concern for the future, Dr. Mitchell points to the following circumstances:

- Recent and more accurate reconstructions of past climates reveal that climate has been variable on all time scales, "as if climate is continually hunting around on equilibrium which it never fully achieves." This, in turn, suggests that future climate will be likely to differ from the present climate.
- Various polluting activities by man are believed capable of bringing about inadvertent climate

changes. The nature and extent of such human influences on climate are not yet fully understood.

- New observational evidence indicates that the world's climate has been cooling gradually during the past thirty years, and in some respects may have become more variable as well.
- Mankind seems to have become increasingly vulnerable to even the smallest of atmospheric changes.

Because of these circumstances, both science and world society are more sensitive than ever before to climatic change. Indeed, alarming visions of impending climate disaster of one kind or another have some popular writers tuned in to the recent discoveries. Yet, say climatologists, such projections are entirely reasonable and proper. Recently, for example, a British television program left the impression that man may be headed for a rapid cooling of global climate. Many people in England were frightened that a "snow blitz" was imminent. Then, within a short time, a new title appeared in bookstores warning mankind of the inevitability of a painful heat death if man persists much longer using energy from conventional fossil and nuclear sources. And, *Science,* one of the most reputable journals in the field, warned that a warming effect by carbon dioxide growth in the atmosphere was well under way. At the same time, the cooling trend of the past thirty years is mentioned as confirmation of approaching catastrophe, as if such cooling will spark the start of a new ice age destined to continue without interruption in one direction.

Sums up Dr. Mitchell,

The media has been having a lot of fun with this situation. Whenever there is a cold wave they seek out a proponent of the ice-age-is-coming school and put his theories on page one. Whenever there is a heat wave, they turn to his opposite number in the greenhouse-warming-school and put his comments on page one. To the man in the street, it all means that mankind is to either freeze or fry. To the more discriminating layman, however, it simply creates something of a credibility gap for science that draws attention away from the more pressing problems of climatic variability and its myriad impacts on society that we would like to, and need to, understand better.

Most climate experts believe that mankind's long-range climate problems will be typical of what has always been known. Those problems will be manageable, rather than unmanageable and extraordinary. It appears that the evaluation of natural climate may not be a deterministic process in time. "If nature could somehow be inter-rogated as to what it plans to look like one hundred years from now," says Dr. Mitchell, "she might have to answer in the form of a set of probabilities of various possible out-comes."

Irrespective of future climatic developments, man will undoubtedly have many choices in his improvement on earth. No scientist knows what our lives will be like in another century or two, but whatever they are, they will undoubtedly have important industrial growth and energy use. Atmospheric scientists insist that it would be foolish to continue the disregard of the '50s, '60s, and '70s, that the future can be gauged by extrapolation of the quasi-exponential growth of the past. There is little doubt that population will increase in the future and will be more active, and more prolific in energy uses. To that extent, we are approaching the day when the climatic impacts of our growth—both industrial and as a species—will compete with the natural climatic forcing mechanisms in determing the course of future climate.

The behavior of the climate system is highly complex. Many more years of serious research will undoubtedly be required to reveal that behavior adequately. In the meantime, the earth is changing. The atmosphere is becoming richer in carbon dioxide by a fraction of a percent every year. Energy use is expanding dramatically, even though the Arab oil embargo is over. Scientists are discovering new pollution problems, such as those related to ozone destruction by nitrogen oxides and chlorofluorocarbons. These portend potentially serious and slow-to-heal impacts on climate.

At the present time, there are no definitive answers to such questions as, "If man were not around to interfere with nature, what would happen in the way of future climatic developments?," "To the extent that nature herself knows the answer to that question, is it within technological grasp to wring the answer from her?" "What are man's intentions with regard to the future?" and, most important, "If it turns out that certain avenues of future societal progress would lead to serious and possible irreversible changes of climate, as a result of inadvertent side effects on the environment, would man realize this in time to avert calamity?"

Until scientists have answers to these questions, and experts insist it is by no means clear when they can expect to have them, meaningful projections of future trends in the climate will remain beyond science's grasp. Scientists can speculate on the risk of another ice age, or on the risk of overheating the earth by overuse of fossil or nuclear energy, but they are not able to quantify those risks to the extent that society requires, if society is to plan for the future on a more rational basis than simply catering to fears of the unknown.

# Glossary

*Advection*—A transfer of atmospheric properties by horizontal movements of air. Compare with convection current.

*Altimeter*—An aneroid barometer calibrated to indicate altitude instead of pressure.

*Altocumulus*—A form of middle cloud.

*Altostratus*—A form of middle cloud.

*Anemometer*—An instrument that measures wind speed.

*Atmosphere*—The envelope of air surrounding the earth.

*Atmospheric pressure*—The force exerted by the weight of the atmosphere on the earth.

*Barometer*—An instrument for measuring atmospheric pressure.

*Celsius*—Currently preferred name for the temperature scale formerly known as centigrade.

*Centigrade*—The temperature scale where water freezes at 0°C and boils at 100°C; also called Celsius.

*Cirrocumulus*—A form of high cloud.

*Cirrostratus*—A form of high cloud.

*Cirrus*—A form of high cloud.

*Cold front*—A discontinuity at the forward edge of an advancing cold-air mass which is displacing warmer air in its path.

*Cumulonimbus*—A form of cloud with extensive vertical development.

*Cumulus*—A form of cloud with less vertical development than cumulonimbus.

*Cyclone*—A closed circulation about a low pressure center which is counterclockwise in the Northern Hemisphere.

*Doldrums*—The equatorial belt of calms or light variable winds lying between the two trade-wind belts.

*Fahrenheit*—A temperature scale on which 32° denotes the temperature of melting ice and 212° denotes the temperature of boiling water, both under standard atmospheric conditions.

*Front*—The zone of transition between two air masses of different density.

*GARP*—Global Atmospheric Research Program.

*Greenhouse effect*—The heating effect exerted by the atmosphere upon the earth by virtue of the fact that the atmosphere (mainly its water vapor) absorbs and reemits infrared radiation.

*High*—An area of high atmospheric pressure that has closed circulation; an anticyclone.

*Humidity*—Generally, some measure of the water vapor content of the air.

*Jet stream*—Relatively strong winds concentrated within a narrow stream in the atmosphere.

*Knot*—The unit of speed in the nautical system; equal to 1 nautical mile per hour.

*Mean temperature*—The average temperature of the air as indicated by a properly exposed thermometer during a given period, usually a day, a month, or a year.

*NASA*—National Aeronautics and Space Administration.

*Occluded front or occlusion*—The front that is formed when and where a cold front overtakes a warm front or a stationary front.

*Ozone*—A nearly colorles gaseous form of oxygen with a characteristic odor like that of weak chlorine. It is found in trace quantities in the atmosphere, primarily above the tropopause.

*Precipitation*—The collective name for moisture, in liquid or solid form, large enough to fall from the atmosphere.

*Prevailing wind*—The wind direction most frequently observed during a given period.

*Psychrometer*—An instrument for measuring atmospheric humidity. It consists of a dry-bulb thermometer and wet-bulb thermometer (covering with a muslin wick) and is used in the calculation of dew point and relative humidity.

*Radar*—An electronic instrument used for the detection and ranging of distant objects which scatter or reflect radio energy.

*Radiosonde*—A balloon-borne instrument for the simultaneous measurement and transmission of meteorological data.

*Rain gauge*—An instrument for measuring rainfall.

*Relative humidity*—The ratio of the amount of moisture in the air to the amount which the air could hold at the same temperature if it were saturated; usually expressed in percent.

*Smog*—A natural fog contaminated by industrial pollutants; a mixture of smoke and fog.

*Solar radiation*—The total electromagnetic radiation emitted by the sun.

*Stratocumulus*—A form of low cloud.

*Stratosphere*—The layer of the atmosphere between the troposphere and the mesosphere where the air is usually stable.

*Stratus*—A form of low cloud.

*Tornado*—A violently rotating column of air attended by a funnel-shaped or tubular cloud hanging beneath a cumulonimbus cloud.

*Trade winds*—Two belts of winds, one on either side of the equatorial doldrums, where the winds blow almost constantly from easterly quadrants.

*Tropical air*—Warm air having its source in the low latitudes, chiefly in the regions of the subtropical, high pressure systems.

*Tropical cyclone*—The preferred name for hurricane. An intense tropical storm with winds exceeding 75 mph.

*Tropopause*—The boundary between the troposphere and stratosphere, usually characterized by an abrupt change in lapse rate.

*Troposhpere*—The lower region of the atmosphere from the ground to the tropopause.

*Turbulence*—Irregular motion of the atmosphere produced when air flows over a comparatively uneven surface, such as the surface of the earth, or when two currents of air flow past or over each other in different directions or at different speeds.

*Typhoon*—A western Pacific place-name for a tropical cyclone.

*Warm front*—The discontinuity at the forward edge of an advancing current of relatively warm air which is displacing a retreating colder air mass.

*Weather*—The short-term variations of the atmosphere in terms of temperature, pressure, wind, moisture, cloudiness, precipitation and visibility.

*Westerlies*—Specifically, the dominant west-to-east motion of the atmosphere centered over the middle latitudes of both hemispheres.

*Zenith*—That point, on any given observer's celestial sphere, which lies directly over his head.

# Bibliography

*Modern Meteorology and Climatology*, T. J. Chandler, Nelson; London 1972.

*Weather and Climate*, R. C. Sutcliffe, Weidenfeld & Nicolson; London 1966.

*Inadvertent Climate Modification: Report of the Study of Man's Impact on Climate*, MIT Press; Cambridge, Mass. and London 1971.

*Useful Applications of Earth-Oriented Satellites: Report of the Central Review Committee*, 1969. Summer Study on Space Applications by National Research Council, Division of Engineering, National Academy of Sciences, Washington, D.C.

"The Natural Breakdown of the Present Interglacial and its Possible Intervention by Human Activities," Mitchell, J. M. Jr. *Quaternary Res.*, 2:436-445, 1973.

*Interaction Between the Atmosphere and the Oceans*, 1962. Report of the Joint Panel on Air-Sea Interaction to the Committee on Atmospheric Sciences and the Committee on Oceanography, NAS-NRC Publ. 983. National Academy of Sciences-National Research Council, Washington, D.C.

*Weather and Climate Modification: Problems and Prospects.* Vol. I, Summary and Recommendations; Vol. II, Research and Development, 1966: Final Report of the Panel on Weather and Climate Modification to the Committee on Atmospheric Sciences, NAS-NRC Publ. 1350. National Academy of Sciences-National Research Council, Washington, D.C.

*Cloud Physics and Cloud Seeding*, Battan, Louis J. Anchor Books, Doubleday: Garden City, NY, 1962.

*The Nature of Violent Storms*, Battan, Louis J. Anchor Books, Doubleday: Garden City, NY, 1961.

*The Unclean Sky: A Meteorologist Looks at Air Pollution*, Battan, Louis J. Anchor Books, Doubleday: Garden City, NY, 1966.

*Watching for the Wind: The Seen and Unseen Influences on Local Weather*, Edinger, James G. Anchor Books, Doubleday: Garden City, NY, 1967.

*Jet Streams: How Do They Affect Our Weather?* Reiter, Elmar R. Anchor Books, Doubleday: Garden City, NY, 1967.

*General Meteorology*, Byers, H. R. McGraw-Hill: New York, 1959, 3rd ed.

# Index

Aerosols, 100, 116, 118, 123

Aerovane transmitter, 41

Africa, drought in, 3, 56

Agassiz, Louis, 50

Agriculture, 2-5, 119; drought-tolerant crops, 62, 69-70; impact of climate on, 89; effects of modification on, 97; productivity, 14, 48, 57, 66, 70, 86-89, 96, 105, 120

Agung, Mount, 13

Air: circulation of, 21, 35, 67, 73; pollution, 4, 78, 97, 113, 120; temperature of, 59. *See also* Atmosphere; Wind

Aircraft, use in data gathering, 99, 108

Alaska, 11, 24, 71

Albedo, 120, 122, 124

Allergies, airborne, 78

Altocumulus clouds, 33

Altostratus clouds, 32

Anemometer, 41

Arthritis, relation to weather, 77

Astrology, 75

Atmosphere, 19, 20; carbon dioxide in, 12, 96-98, 100, 114, 118, 134, 140, 142; changes in, 34, 40, 77; circulation of, 27, 44, 66, 71, 84; function of, 35; heating of, 2, 40, 142; interaction with human body, 75; interaction with oceans, 43, 47, 122, 125; modification, effects of, 97; physical characteristics of, 21; pressure, 70, 73, 79, 84; pollution in, 96, 133; solar radiation distribution, 115; turbidity in, 98; virus transport, 77; water in, 36. *See also* Climate; Weather

Barometric pressure, 41, 77, 82

Bering Sea, 71

Biosphere, 20, 26

Biotropic changes, 71, 72

Birth, effect of weather on, 79

Bohr, Niels, 16

Bonneville, Lake, 51

Brooks, C. E. P., 52

Brooks, Harvey, 81

Bubonic plague, 79

Burroughs, Edgar Rice, 15

Cape Cod, 49

Carbon dioxide, in atmosphere, 12, 96-98, 100, 114, 118, 134, 140, 142

Carbon monoxide, 13

Celsus, 75

Champlain, Lake, 51

Chlorofluorocarbons, 142

Cirrocumulus clouds, 29

Cirrostratus clouds, 31

Cirrus clouds, 32

Cirques, 24

Climate: classification of, 68; definition of, 19, 34, 139; dependency on, 3; fluctuations, 3, 4, 89, 116-121, l31, 140; effect of astronomical variation on, 18; effect on food supplies, 3; effect on livestock, 58; effect of volcanic dust on, 14; history of, 12, 40, 121, 134, 139; information analysis of, 136; interaction with agriculture, 57, 89; interaction with human body, 75; interaction with ocean, 18, 43, 47, 122, 125; internal controls, 40, 42, 122; man's interference with. *See* Environmental Problems, man-made; models for, 47, 83, 88, 121; modification of, 81,